FOR GOOD MEASURE

The Story of Modern Measurement

MELVIN BERGER

FOR GOOD MEASURE

The Story of
Modern Measurement

illustrated by Adolph E. Brotman

McGRAW-HILL BOOK COMPANY
New York • Toronto • London • Sydney

For her invaluable help this book is dedicated to my wife,
Gilda, a treasure without measure.

Acknowledgments

MANY SCIENTISTS AND WORKERS in the field of measurement generously assisted in the preparation of this book by checking its scientific accuracy and by involving me in the excitement and challenge of modern measurement.

The staff of the National Bureau of Standards was most cooperative. Mr. A. V. Gentilini and Mr. J. F. Reilly, of the Office of Public Information, arranged visits to the various laboratories of the National Bureau, and provided me with much interesting information. In addition, several scientists at the National Bureau took time from their heavy schedules to read through the parts of the manuscript that touched on their fields of specialization, making valued comments and suggestions.

Dr. Donald Baird of the General Telephone and Electronics Laboratory also was most kind, reviewing and commenting on the entire manuscript.

The following laboratories and scientific companies sent me material relating to the tools and methods of modern measurement, and replied to my questions: Bell Telephone Laboratories (H. E. Apfelbaum), Bulova Watch Company, Electric Thermometer (Kurt Bissing), Gaertner Scientific Corporation (Edgar W. Bolles), General Electric Research and Development Center (Peter Van Avery), Harrel, Inc.

Acknowledgments 6

(H. E. Harris), Hewlett Packard, IBM Research Division (D. E. Udell), Macalaster Scientific Corporation, Moeller Instrument Corporation (James Mark), Phoenix Precision Company (Horst K. Blume), Pyrometer Instrument Company (Paul V. Bollerman), RCA Laboratories (Phyllis Smith), Rockwell Manufacturing Company (C. A. Mauthie), Thermo Electric (Robert A. Norman), Trans Sonics (Robert L. Blanchard), United States Naval Observatory (R. Glenn Hall), and Varian Associates (Arthur O. McCoulrey).

To all those who have been of such great help, I would like to express my sincere gratitude. Their concern and interest has made this a better book, although I, of course, assume full responsibility for its contents.

Melvin Berger

Contents

Prologue

"MAN LEARNS TO SPLIT THE ATOM!"
"ROCKET TO THE MOON!"
"RADIO SIGNALS RECEIVED FROM STARS."

These are some of the dramatic science headlines of the twentieth century. Behind each of these stories, and many others as well, is another story. It is the story of how advances in the science of measurement made the discovery possible.

Every scientist is part measurement scientist. Before it was possible to split the atom, there had to be ways to measure neutron flow. Before the new rockets could go into space, there had to be a thermometer to measure the -412 degrees of the liquid hydrogen fuel. Before signals could be received from space, the giant radio antennas had to be measured to within a fraction of an inch. Measurement plays an important role in every branch of science.

But measurement is not only for science and scientists. Modern industry, too, needs reliable measurement. A jet airplane engine will work only if the hundreds of individual parts have been most carefully measured to fit together. Each can of yellow house paint must be the same shade and quality as every other can of yellow paint made by the same company. And no baker could stay in business unless every one-pound loaf of bread that he sells weighs exactly one pound.

You, also, depend on measurement in your daily life.

You look at a clock to measure time, a ruler to measure length, a thermometer to measure temperature, a scale to measure weight, and so on. Can you guess how many times a day you make a measurement of some sort? It has been estimated that every single person in the country makes an average of ten measurements daily!

All of these measurements are based on the science of precise and accurate measurement, called metrology. Its scientists are called metrologists. Their devotion to the science of measurement has brought metrology to its present high levels.

As an example, look at the accuracy of modern measurement in length, mass, time, and temperature, the four basic measurements. Length measurement, using a beam of light as the measuring scale, is accurate to one part in 100 million. Modern balances make mass measurements that are also accurate to one part in 100 million. Time is measured by an atomic clock that will not gain or lose a second in 30,000 years. The various electric thermometers measure temperature to an accuracy of one part in a million.

One can only marvel at what the metrologists have already achieved. Yet they are not satisfied. They continue to search for new ways and means of measuring with greater accuracy, greater precision, greater reliability. The joy, the excitement, and the challenge of modern metrology comes from striving for higher and higher levels of measurement skill.

one ■ *You and Measurement*

We think of our body in many different ways—as something that hurts when we are sick, something that looks pretty when it moves with grace, and something that tingles after a cold shower—but we seldom think of it as a scientific tool. Yet our body is a most remarkable piece of scientific equipment, able to make many kinds of measurements.

For instance, touch the period at the end of this sentence. Easy, isn't it? However, your eyes have to measure the distance to the book, and find the exact position of the period on the page. Your arm and hand muscles then have to measure how much to push or pull to get to the point that your eyes have located.

What about measuring with your ears? The next time you chat with your friends compare the sounds you hear. Who speaks with a loud voice and who speaks with a soft voice? Who has a high-pitched voice and whose voice is low in pitch?

Touch some objects around you. Are they hard or soft, rough or smooth? Pick some things up. Which are heavier and which are lighter? Without looking at a clock, can you estimate how long you have been reading?

All of these measurements are based on the use of the

senses. Through the senses you receive messages of all sorts from outside, as well as from within, your body. It has been accepted from ancient times that we have five basic senses—seeing, hearing, smelling, tasting, and feeling. The secondary senses recognize heat and cold, pain, hunger, thirst, gravity, and muscle movement.

As you know, your body is composed of millions and millions of individual cells, each with its own role to play. Among these cells there are some whose job it is to receive messages. Some of these receiver cells recognize the brightness and color of light; others recognize pitch and loudness of sounds. Still others recognize odors, tastes, textures, weight, temperature, and many other messages. Each of these messages is called a stimulus. The cells that receive the stimuli (plural of stimulus) are called sense receptors.

Each sense receptor changes the stimulus it receives, whether it be a light, a sound, or whatever, into a tiny electrical impulse. Connected to each of the sense receptors is a nerve cell, or neuron, which is usually a threadlike cell that might be up to three feet long. The neuron's job is to carry the electrical impulse from the sense receptor to the brain. In the brain the electrical impulse is interpreted so that you can recognize the original stimulus. It is estimated that the impulses travel through the neurons at the rate of 200 miles per hour. If you dip your big toe into hot bath water, your brain knows about it approximately one-sixtieth of a second later!

Seeing

Your eyes make possible the sense of sight. Before your eyes can see, however, there must be light. The light, either directly from the sun or from a light bulb, or indirectly reflected from an object, enters your eye through a transparent lens. The lens focuses, or brings to a point, the light rays that enter your eye.

After passing through the lens, the light goes through the transparent liquid that fills your eyeball, and falls on the back wall of the eyeball, which is the retina. The retina is lined with perhaps a million sense receptor cells that are sensitive to light. There are two types of receptors: cones and rods. Most of the seeing, and all color vision, depends on the cones. The rods seem to function only as an aid to seeing in very dim light.

The cones and rods are connected to a series of nerve cells which eventually are woven together to form a cable

that goes to the brain. This cable, which contains about one million nerve cells, is called the optic nerve.

One of the most important uses of your sense of sight is to measure distance. Your eyes, a few inches apart as they are, enable you to get two, slightly different, views of the same object. Your brain is then able to combine these views to produce one image in depth.

You can test the advantage of having two eyes with this experiment. Place two coins on a table, and hold your head so that your eyes are level with the table top. Now arrange the coins so that they are at exactly the same distance from you, but not touching. Your two eyes allow you to do this with little difficulty.

Next, try the same experiment, but this time keep one eye closed. You should find this much more difficult, if not impossible. The lack of perspective from just one eye cuts your ability to perform this apparently easy task.

A variation of this experiment requires the help of a friend. Ask your friend to stand about three feet away from you, holding a pencil with the point toward you at the height of his waist. Take another pencil and using both eyes try to touch the tip of his pencil with yours. It should be rather easy. Now try it with one eye closed, and you will again notice how difficult it is to measure distance with only one eye.

Many of the measurements that you make with your eyes also require experience and intelligence. You know, for example, that the farther away an object is, the smaller its apparent size, even though its actual size does not change at all. In other words, as you watch an automobile going down the road it appears smaller and smaller. Since the road also seems narrower, and the houses and people along the road seem smaller, you realize that this is just an appearance. You know that the car remains the same size.

Familiar objects make it possible to measure distance by apparent size. Your eyes, though, can sometimes be fooled. In this picture, which figure is the tallest?

Most people would say figure 1. Actually, they are all the same height in the picture. The road and house and trees are misleading, and make the first figure seem taller. Cover the deceiving clues and you can easily see that all three figures are the same size.

Hearing

The human ear can hear a sound one trillion times louder than the softest sound it can detect.   This is quite a remarkable spread.   It is all the more remarkable when you realize that there is no man-made measuring tool that can measure directly over such a wide range.

The organ of hearing is, of course, the ear.   Actually, we see just the outer ear.   The outer ear takes the sound

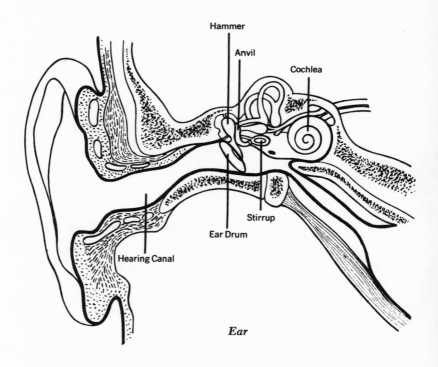

Ear

waves that are in the form of vibrating air particles, gathers them together, and sends them to the middle and inner ears through the hearing canal. At the inner end of the hearing canal is the ear drum, or tympanum, a very flexible membrane stretched over the hearing canal. The vibrating air particles set the sensitive ear drum into vibration.

Behind the ear drum are the hammer, anvil, and stirrup, the three smallest bones in the body. The hammer is attached to the ear drum. It passes the vibrations on to the anvil and stirrup, the vibrations getting stronger as they go from bone to bone.

From the stirrup the vibrations pass to the cochlea in the inner ear. The cochlea is about one inch long, and is shaped like a snail's shell. It is filled with liquid, and its inner surface is covered with nerve endings. The nerve cells change the mechanical movement caused by the vibrations of the air particles into small electrical currents. These nerve impulses go to the brain, where they give the sensation of sound.

Sounds are measured in several different ways. One quality we listen for is loudness. When you play a phonograph or television, you adjust the volume control so that you can hear the music or speech at a natural level. When you play an instrument in an orchestra or sing in a chorus, you listen to yourself to check how loud you sound and to hear whether or not you are blending in with the others.

The loudness of sound is determined by how wide the vibrations are. To put it another way, the pressure of the air particles striking your ear drum determines loudness. Louder sounds produce stronger pressures; softer sounds produce weaker pressures. As the sound vibrations move through the air, though, they get weaker and weaker. The more distant the sound source, the softer the sound.

With the help of a friend you can test how well your ear measures loudness. Sit in a chair alongside a table in a very quiet room. Lay a yardstick on the table pointing away from you.

First, have your friend hold a watch near your ear. Do not look as he slowly moves it away along the yardstick. Tell him the moment you no longer hear the tick. Let him note the distance at which the sound becomes inaudible to you. Then reverse the procedure. Have your friend place the watch quite far from you and ask him to move it slowly toward you along the yardstick. Report the moment the watch ticks become audible. Compare the results.

Finally, have your friend move the watch slowly toward you from the point at which it is just audible. Call out as soon as you hear a difference in loudness. How many inches did he move it before you detected a change? Per-

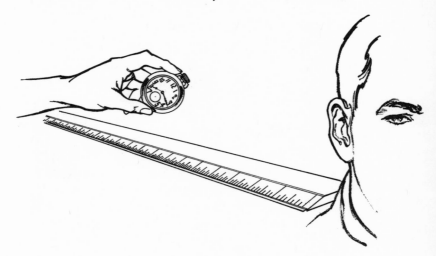

form all of these experiments several times, and average the results to get the most accurate figures possible.

Turn your chair around now and repeat the three parts of the experiment with your other ear. Make an average of the results. Compare these results with the results for the first ear. Were the figures the same or was there much difference? Perhaps your friend will want to have both of his ears tested to determine how accurately his ears measure changes in loudness.

Your ears also measure how low or high a sound is, which is called pitch. While loudness depends on the strength of the vibrations, pitch depends on the speed of the vibrations, or frequency. The greater the frequency with which the compressed air particles strike the ear drum, the higher the pitch; the lower the frequency, the lower the pitch.

With the help of a friend and the use of a piano you can test your ability to recognize difference in pitch. Turn your back to the piano and have your friend play one low-pitched note (on his extreme left as he faces the piano), and one high-pitched note (on his extreme right). This will help to establish the basic difference in sound between low and high pitch.

Now let him mix them up. Sometimes he should play the high note first and sometimes the low note first. You decide each time which came first. Each pair of notes should be closer together than the pair before, until he is playing notes right next to each other. The high and low notes that are far apart in pitch are easier to recognize than the notes that are very close in pitch.

Your ear also measures direction. You are able to do this because your ears are several inches apart and face in opposite directions. The two ears hear sounds slightly differently. You hear a sound coming from off to your right a little louder and a little earlier in your right ear than in your left ear. Likewise, you hear a sound coming from the left louder and earlier in your left ear. This difference, as interpreted by your brain, enables you to judge the direction of the sound source.

Your ears, placed as they are on the sides of your head, make it easier to measure the direction of the sound than the height of the sound. Close your eyes and ask a friend to hold a watch in various positions around your head. You will find it quite easy to measure how far it is off to a side, but rather difficult to judge its height.

Time

There are several ways in which the body acts as a clock, enabling us to measure time. We are all aware of the ticks of our heartbeats and pulse. We also know our timetable of hunger and thirst and sleepiness. It is believed that our inner biological clock is controlled by electrical and chemical reactions in the brain.

The ability to use your body to measure time varies very much from person to person, and from time to time. It is thought that early man had a very finely developed sense of time, but that the discovery of fire upset his inner clock by making it possible to turn the darkness of night into bright light.

How well can you use your body clock to measure time? Look at the second hand of a clock or watch, and at one point close your eyes as you note the position of the hand. Without counting to yourself, open your eyes when you feel ten seconds have passed. How close were you? Try this with some friends and see how well their bodies can measure time.

There are circumstances which tend to throw off your body's clock. In France, for example, in 1906, several miners were trapped in a coal mine for three weeks. When they were rescued, each of the men insisted that he had been trapped for only four or five days.

You yourself know the immense difference there seems to be between an hour of fun at a party and an hour in a dull class. Albert Einstein summed it up best in his explanation of the Theory of Relativity: When a man sits with a pretty girl for an hour it seems to him a minute. But let him sit on a hot stove for only a minute, and it seems longer than an hour. That's relativity!

Your body makes measurements in several other ways. Your skin measures the temperature around you. When it is too hot the blood vessels in your skin come to the surface to radiate some of the excess heat into the air. When it is too cold the blood vessels sink deeper into the skin to preserve their heat. In addition, when the skin feels the temperature is getting too high it starts to perspire, and as the perspiration evaporates, the skin is cooled.

There is, however, a way to fool your body's temperature sense. Fill three pans with water—one very hot, one very cold, and one lukewarm. Place a finger of one hand in the hot water and a finger of the other hand in the cold water.

After about one minute, plunge both fingers into the lukewarm water. How does the temperature of the water feel to the finger coming from the hot water? How does it feel to the finger coming from the cold water? The temperature seems different to each finger because of the temperature of the water it was in before. After hot, the warm water feels cold; after cold, the warm water feels hot.

By measuring the pressure on your skin and the strain on your muscles you can usually estimate the weight of an object, as well as its hardness or stiffness. By sniffing you can compare how strong or weak different odors are. Can you think of any other ways in which you use your body for measuring?

Summary

The body is truly a remarkable measuring instrument. It is remarkable for the many things it can measure, from size to pitch, from smell to taste, from weight to time. It is equally remarkable for the wide range of measurements it can make, from bright to dark, from loud to soft, from heavy to light.

Modern science has developed many very impressive measuring tools. As you look at these tools in the following chapters, you will find that most of them are closely related to our senses. A few, such as the ruler or scale, allow us to express in inches or pounds measurements we can only guess at with our senses. Most of the others extend our senses beyond their normal range. Only the measuring tools for electrical current and atomic radiation deal with measurements completely beyond the human senses.

two ■ *A Measure of Progress*

VERY EARLY MAN had little or no need for measurement. He was a nomad, always on the move. His caves or simple tents did not require him to measure timbers or other building materials. There were no fields to measure for planting. He grew or made all that he needed, and did not have to measure or weigh for purposes of trade.

It was much later, about ten thousand years ago, that man first had a need to measure. By then some men had settled in one place, and had started to farm and raise animals. Land had to be measured and boundaries had to be set. It was not possible to grow or make all the things that were necessary for life.

The farmer wanted to trade his extra cow for his neighbor's extra grain. The fur trapper wanted to trade his animal skins for the woodsman's lumber. And man needed measurement to help with his construction of houses and boats.

Units and Standards

Before he could measure, though, he needed some thing, a *unit*, that he could compare with the object being measured. To measure the length of a field, he might chose the length of his foot. He could then find the length of the field by counting the number of foot-long steps. To judge the weight of a jewel, he might use a grain of wheat. The number of grains of wheat which would balance the jewel would be a measure of the weight of the jewel.

Units are lengths, or weights, or whatever, that are used for measuring. All measurement consists of comparing the unit with the object being measured. There is a serious problem, though, in using natural units for measuring. The units are not always the same. One man might measure a field, and find it is 20 "feet" long. Another man, with a longer foot, might find it is only 18 "feet" long. Still another man, with a very short foot, might measure it as 23 "feet" long. How could people agree on the length of a foot?

In ancient Greece and Rome each ruler decreed that the length of his foot was the official foot. He had a piece of wood cut that was exactly as long as his foot. This stick became the *standard*, the actual physical copy of the unit.

But as time went on, weights and measures got more and more confused. Each country, in fact, each city and town, had its own units and standards. Farmers, traders, scientists, builders, all those who depended on measurement, felt a need for order. They wanted a system that would organize measurement.

The Metric System

The first effort to introduce a single, logical, universal system of measurement came in the late eighteenth century. Scientific leaders who followed in the wake of the French Revolution wanted to apply logic and scientific thinking to every aspect of life. The French set out to create a new measurement system, with all units to be based on some unchanging natural measurement. And the arithmetic was to be based on the number 10, for quick and easy calculations.

The natural unit they chose was one ten-millionth of the length of an imaginary line from the North Pole to the Equator, that passed through Paris. They called this unit the *meter*, and the entire system the metric system, since all other units were derived from the meter. The meter came to be 39.37 of our inches. The French constructed a platinum bar of that length which became the standard meter.

The unit of mass, the *kilogram*, they defined as the weight of the water at 41 degrees Fahrenheit contained in a cube measuring one-tenth of a meter in each dimension (3.937 inches by 3.937 inches by 3.937 inches). The water temperature was specified since this is the temperature at which water is most dense, that is, weighs the most. The kilogram equals just over 2.2 of our pounds. The French also constructed a platinum cylinder, 1.5 inches in height and diameter, as the standard of mass.

After the French scientists had devised the metric system and built the standards, they found that the line through Paris was actually 102.4 feet longer than they originally believed. And further, they found that the standard meter bar was slightly shorter than it should have been. It was, however, too late to change the entire system. The first platinum bar, rather than the line through Paris, is the standard on which the metric system is based.

All units in the metric system are related by the number 10. For the larger units, Greek prefixes are used. As an example, a *deca*meter is 10 meters, a *hecto*meter is 100 meters, a *kilo*meter is 1,000 meters, and so on.

For the smaller units, Latin prefixes are used. A *deci*-meter is one-tenth meter, a *centi*meter is one-hundredth meter, a *milli*meter is one-thousandth meter, and so on. These prefixes are used with the other metric units as well.

In 1799 the metric system became the legal system of weights and measures in France. The French were so unwilling to accept the new measurements, though, that the metric system had to be dropped. It was not until 1840, nearly fifty years after its first acceptance, that the metric system finally became the permanent measurement system of France. The logical, easy-to-use system spread through most of Europe, except Great Britain, and has become the measuring system of scientists throughout the world.

United States Weights and Measures

While the metric system was being developed in France, the United States was becoming a nation. One of the first concerns of the Founding Fathers was the establishment of a system of weights and measures. In the 1776 Articles of Confederation the Continental Congress was given the task of "fixing the standard of weights and measures throughout the united states." The Constitution later gave this power to Congress. George Washington's very first message to Congress in 1790 said: "Uniformity in the currency, weights and measures of the United States is an object of great importance. . . ."

Thomas Jefferson, then Secretary of State, was asked to report on the matter. He suggested adopting either the English system, with the units of yard, pound, and gallon, or the French metric system. Not knowing which to choose, Congress decided to wait.

Year after year passed. Then, because of the close ties with England, a brass duplicate of the English pound weight was brought to the United States in 1827. It was deposited in the Philadelphia mint and used as a standard for making coins. Over the following years two bronze yardsticks were also brought over from England. The United States Congress finally passed laws to make the English pound and yard United States standards.

Although the United States Congress did pass a law in 1866 allowing the use of the metric system, it did not insist that it be used. The old English system, which had been much improved and standardized by then, remained the system in use in the United States. Scientists, though, prefer the metric system and use it almost entirely for advanced scientific work.

Nine years later, in 1875, the International Bureau of Weights and Measures was established in Sèvres, near Paris, France. New, more accurate copies of the metric standards were made. One meter bar and one kilogram weight were placed in a sealed vault beneath the International Bureau at Sèvres. Three keys are needed to unlock the vault door. Each key is kept by a different official of the Bureau, and all three must be present to open the heavy steel doors.

The standards were distributed to countries around the world. There were thirty-one meter bars made, using a mixture of 90 per cent platinum and 10 per cent iridium which would not rust and would not change in length. They were slightly longer than a meter, with engraved lines to mark off the exact meter length. In cross section the bar was in the shape of the letter X to avoid any bending or sagging. Meter bars numbered 21 and 27 were sent to the United States.

Forty standard kilogram weights were also made. The kilogram (1,000 grams) is used as the standard of weight because the gram is so small, weighing only 0.035 ounces. Weights numbered 4 and 20 were sent across the Atlantic too.

In 1893, meter bar 27 and kilogram 20 were made the official standards for all length and weight measurements in the United States. They can be seen by all visitors to the laboratories of the National Bureau of Standards at Gaithersburg, Maryland.

National Bureau of Standards

The National Bureau of Standards was established in 1901 to maintain and improve the standards for the entire country. This Bureau is responsible for over fifty different standards. There are the four basic standards— length, time, mass, and temperature—from which all the other standards are derived. These include standards for measuring speed, volume, neutron flow, magnetism, voltage, humidity, and many more. Speed, for example, is expressed as a unit of length per unit of time, such as miles per hour. Volume is expressed as length cubed. These are derived standards because they all refer to one or more of the four basic standards.

Over the years since its founding, the National Bureau of Standards has been the leading laboratory for advancing all aspects of the science of metrology. Scientists at the Bureau have studied problems that range from advanced nuclear physics, to determining the best red and green tints for traffic lights, to the longest-lasting material for shoe soles. The story of modern measurement is very much the story of the National Bureau of Standards.

Every measurement in the United States, from the wooden ruler used in the first grade classroom to the atomic clock at the Naval Observatory, is either directly or indirectly derived from one of the basic standards maintained by the Bureau.

The figures on the money being spent on measurement are astounding. About 25 billion dollars is invested in measuring tools, and 4½ billion dollars is being added every year. About 20 billion dollars is invested in measurement research, with 3 billion dollars being added each year. Altogether, the annual United States investment in measurement is about 50 billion dollars!

The scientists at the National Bureau of Standards, though devoted to learning how to measure with the highest possible accuracy and precision, are the first to insist that there is no such thing as a perfect measurement. They agree that all measurement is approximate. Never can it be said that the temperature is exactly 72 degrees or that some event lasted exactly 19 minutes. Never is the object or value being measured exactly equal to the units being used—no matter how small the units.

In discussing the advances in metrology made at the Bureau, the scientists are always very careful to observe the different meanings of the words *accuracy* and *precision*. Accuracy tells how close the result is to the true value of a measurement. Precision tells how close to a true answer the tools and methods of the measurement will allow the result to be.

For example, the weather bureau says that the temperature is 47 degrees. You take a thermometer from your house, and find that it reads 52 degrees when you get it

outside.   Your result is not *accurate* because you did not
allow enough time for the thermometer to reach the
true temperature.   On the other hand, if your thermometer is marked only every five degrees, the precision is lim-
ited by that fact.   Your measurement could not be more
precise than to within five degrees.

Errors of accuracy come from carelessness or mistakes of
the person doing the measuring.   Errors of precision are
the limits of the tools or conditions of the particular measurement.

National Measurement System

The latest project of the National Bureau of Standards is
a study of the measurement activities of the country as a
single system.   With this idea of a national measurement
system they hope to understand even better the relation-
ships between the different measurements.   And they
hope that the Bureau will then be able to play its central
role in serving and improving the system.

The Bureau's services are developing standards and
measurement techniques for three basic purposes: to provide a complete and uniform system of measurement expressed in common units and methods of use; to provide
reliable, precise data on the properties of different materials; and to furnish information on the performance characteristics of various materials and products.

The national measurement system guarantees that a battery made in California, a transistor made in Kansas, a
loudspeaker made in Ohio, and wire made in Florida can
be assembled into a radio in New York, with each part fit-
ting and working with the others.   This is possible only
with a linked, accurate national system of measurement.

The National Bureau of Standards is also applying its measurement skills to highly complex problems, such as improving transportation within a large city. The scientists survey the existing roads, railroads, and bus lines to see how well they serve the city. How many people does each carry, how fast, and at what cost? They study the people who are involved. Where do they live, where do they work, what do they do for recreation, and which form of transportation do they prefer? Finally, the scientists project all of their data into the future, so that they can make practical suggestions for improvement.

Other studies are being made of entire industries, such as the textile industry, or the effects on the aircraft industry of introducing the supersonic airplane. Part of the National Bureau staff is studying the national measurement system and these other complex problems. Many others, though, are concerned with the more fundamental part of the Bureau's work. They are occupied with advancing and improving the standards and methods of modern measurement.

three ▪ *Length Measurement*

MEASURING LENGTH has a long history, an interesting present, and a promising future. For thousands of years length measurements were confused and uncertain. Then, in 1799, the metric system was devised, and a unit of length measurement, the meter, was chosen. A metal meter bar became the international standard of length. Length measurements throughout the world depended on this standard.

In 1960, to meet the need for ever-greater accuracy, the wavelength of a beam of light became the new standard. Within the next few years it is likely that the laser will replace the light-beam standard. And it is foreseeable that even the laser will be replaced by another, as yet unknown, standard of length.

Feet to Fathoms

We all know the Bible story of Noah and the Ark. What a remarkable carpenter and shipbuilder Noah must have been! He built a ship big enough to hold all the animals, and able to stay afloat during the worst rainstorm and flood in all history. And he built the Ark long before there were any yardsticks or rulers. He was just told to make it 300 cubits long, 50 cubits wide, and 30 cubits high.

Noah knew that the *cubit* was the length of a man's arm, from his elbow to the tip of his middle finger. It was roughly 18 inches in length. Therefore, Noah's Ark was about 450 feet long, 75 feet wide, and 45 feet high.

The cubit was based on the length of the arm. The measurement based on the length of the foot is, of course, called a *foot*. Since both the cubit and foot used a part of the body, they varied very much from person to person. A big person had a long cubit and a long foot. A small person had a short cubit and a short foot.

From studies of old buildings and old writings, it is now believed that the ancient Egyptian cubit was about 21 inches long, the ancient Roman cubit was 17.5 inches long, and the Hebrew cubit was 17.58 inches long. In the same way the foot length varied from ancient Greece, where it was 11.5 inches, to ancient Egypt, where it was 13.76 inches.

As civilization advanced, efforts were made to establish

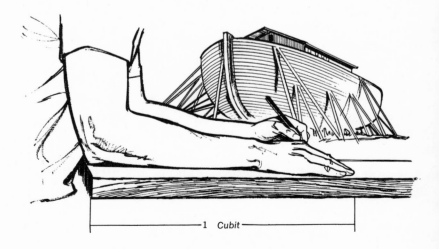

├─1 Cubit─┤

a true standard foot. The English were among the first to try. The story is that one Sunday morning around the year 1120, King Henry I lined up the first twelve men leaving his church, and measured the total length of their feet. He divided their total length by 12. The result he called the official English foot.

The *inch*, the smallest length unit in the English system of measurement, started out as the width of a man's thumb. Since there are about twelve thumb widths in a foot, the English called each one an *unch*, which comes from the Roman word for one-twelfth, *uncia*. In time unch became inch. In 1305, King Edward I of England redefined the inch as "three grains of barley, dry and round, placed end to end lengthwise."

The old Saxon belt, called a gird, gave rise to the modern *yard*. King Henry redefined the yard as the distance from the tip of his royal nose to his thumb, with his arm outstretched to the side. In the fourteenth century, King Edward I had the first standard iron yardstick made, called the Iron Ulna. Ulna, which means elbow in Latin, is the name of a bone in the forearm. The yard was twice the length of the forearm, measured from the elbow to the tip of the middle finger.

The *mile* is a unit of length first used by the ancient Romans. The Roman legions that conquered so much of Europe measured long distances by counting the paces of the marching soldiers. A pace, which contains two steps, equals five feet. The Roman expression for 1,000 paces was *milia passuum*. From this came our word mile, which was originally 5,000 feet long.

For measuring off lengths the early English often used a 16½-foot strip of wood called a *rod*. Its length had been set in the Middle Ages. A sixteenth-century account explained: "To find the length of a measuring rod the right way . . . take sixteen men, short men and tall ones as they leave church and let each of them put one shoe after the other and the length thus obtained shall be a just and common measuring rod to survey the land with." Most farms in old England were made up of one or more fields that measured 40 rods long and one rod wide. Since the furrows made by the plow ran the length of the field, a furrow-long distance, or *furlong*, was equal to 40 rods, or 660 feet.

Eight furlongs, or 5,280 feet, is just a bit longer than the old Roman mile of 5,000 feet. It was therefore decided, in the sixteenth century, to redefine the mile as 5,280 feet, exactly eight furlongs.

And finally, an old length measurement still used by sailors is the *fathom*. It is the distance from fingertip to fingertip with the arms outstretched. The name comes from the Danish, *faedm*, which means outstretched arms. It was originally set as 79.20 inches, which is an immense stretch. Now it is accepted as 72 inches, or 6 feet.

The Meter: A Universal Measure of Length

The standard unit of length accepted by most scientists is the *meter*. Standard meter bars are kept in special vaults at national laboratories throughout the world.

Length measurements in each country are related back to the national standard meter bars by means of the *linear comparator*. In this instrument, the standard is compared with the measuring scales that are used for the actual measurements in laboratories and factories. Highly precise measuring scales from all over the country are sent to the National Bureau of Standards to be checked in the linear comparator.

In the United States the standard meter bar is kept in the Museum of the National Bureau of Standards. When it is to be compared with a measuring scale both objects are placed in the linear comparator the day before the measurements are to be made. In this way, both the bar and the scale are at the same temperature. A difference in temperature would cause one or the other to expand or contract.

The standard bar and the scale being measured are placed side by side in the comparator. Two microscopes on the comparator are then used to compare their lengths.

Most manufacturing plants use a set of *gage blocks* as the measuring scale for their most exacting length measurements. Gage blocks are highly polished blocks of stainless steel. They come in sets of 81 blocks of different lengths from 4 inches to 0.5 inches. They can be combined and added to make any desired length.

Suppose a toolmaker wants to drill a hole 4.750 inches deep. He places a 3-inch, a 1-inch, and a 0.750-inch gage block on top of one another. He adjusts the drill so that it is the same height as the combined gage blocks.

But how can the toolmaker measure the diameter of the

Gage Blocks

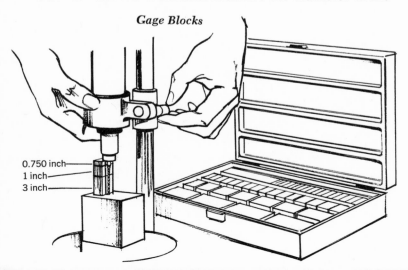

0.750 inch
1 inch
3 inch

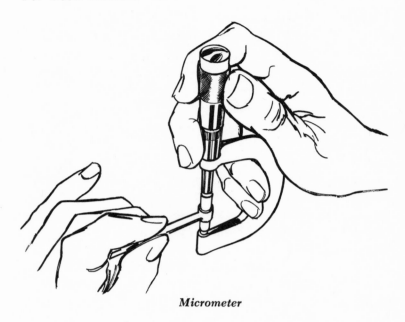

Micrometer

drill? He cannot use the gage blocks. For this kind of measurement he uses a *micrometer*.

The micrometer is shaped like a big question mark. He puts the opening of the micrometer around the drill. Then he adjusts the size of the opening to fit tightly around the drill by means of a screw on the micrometer. A scale on the screw part of the micrometer then shows the diameter of the drill. Some micrometers can measure with a precision of $\frac{1}{10,000}$ of an inch.

Another difficult problem in some industries is to measure the thickness of some material, such as sheet metal, as it is being made. In these cases a *radiation thickness gauge* may be used. A source of atomic radiation, such as a radioactive isotope, is placed under a radiation counter.

It registers the amount of radiation being received. Materials of different thickness are placed between the source and the counter. In most cases, the thicker the material, the less the radiation that passes through. The drop in radiation received by the counter is a measure of the thickness of the material.

By the middle of the twentieth century, length measurements, both by the metrologist in the standards laboratory and by the engineer in the factory, were quite accurate and reliable. But the metrologists were not satisfied with the levels they had reached. (They never are!) They continued their search for new tools, new methods, and new standards that would advance their science.

Then, in 1960, length measurements took a dramatic leap forward. The standard of length became a beam of light! No longer did all length measurements refer back to a metal bar that might be lost or damaged or stolen. The new standard would never change in length, could

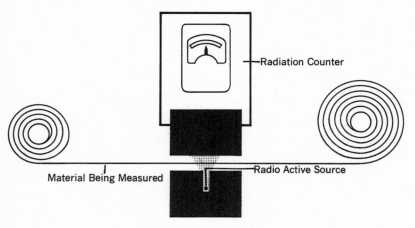

Radiation Thickness Gauge

never be destroyed, and could be reproduced in any laboratory, anywhere in the world.

But how do you measure with a beam of light?

Krypton 86: Measuring With Light

Light, as you know, is energy that travels in waves, with crests and troughs. The waves are measured from any point on one wave to the same point on the next wave.

One of the first scientists to standardize wavelength measurements was Anders Jonas Ångström (1814–1874). In his honor, one of the units of light wave measurement, one ten-millionth of a millimeter, or 0.000000004 inches, was named the angstrom.

Most light sources, such as the sun or electric light bulbs, emit light of many different wavelengths. Scientists realized that to measure with light, they would need a source that emitted light of only one wavelength. This wavelength could then become a new unit of length.

For many years scientists struggled to find the best light source. There were many heated discussions and scientific arguments, as different laboratories and different countries fought for their choice.

Finally, in 1960, an international group of scientists decided that the best source of light would come from passing a current of electricity through the gas krypton, which is found in small quantities in the air. Krypton was chosen because it produces a pure light of only one wavelength. Of the various weights, or isotopes, of krypton that exist, krypton with an atomic mass of 86 was selected. Even more specifically, the orange-red light of krypton 86, with a wavelength of 6,057.80 angstroms, was chosen.

To measure with krypton, the scientist introduces a

small quantity of the gas into a sealed glass tube, from which all of the air has been removed. He places the tube in a bath of liquid nitrogen, at −345 degrees Fahrenheit. The exceedingly low temperature limits the movement of the krypton atoms, and helps to create a light beam with a steady, unchanging wavelength. He then passes an electric current through the tube, and the krypton 86 emits a faint orange glow, with a wavelength of 6,057.80 angstroms.

Light waves are similar in some ways to waves in water. Have you ever seen an incoming ocean wave meet a wave that is being reflected back from the beach or a sea wall? When the incoming crest meets the reflected crest, together they create an even higher crest. The two waves interfere with each other, but since the two crests come together they add to each other's strength, making a still higher crest.

On the other hand, have you ever watched rough water with many waves, and seen points or lines where the water seems smooth and calm? Where the crest of one wave

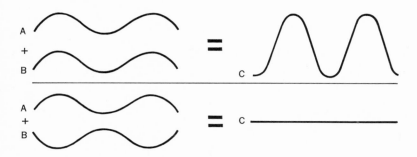

meets the trough of another wave, they cancel each other out.   The water remains smooth at that place.

Light waves also interfere.   When two trains of light waves are joined together under certain circumstances, they form an interference pattern of light and dark sections.   Where the crests come together the light is brighter; where the crest and trough meet each other, the light is dimmer.   By means of the interference pattern of a beam of light of known wavelength, the most precise length measurements could be made.

The interferometer uses interference patterns to make extremely fine length measurements.   This instrument divides the light into two separate beams, and then brings them together again.   At the point at which they are joined, interference between the beams produces a pattern of dark and light bands.   It is this interference pattern that is used for the actual measuring.

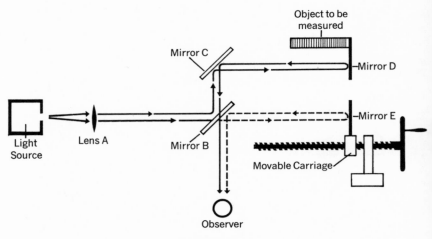

Interferometer

There are dozens of different types of interferometers, but this is the basic scheme of how they work: The light of one wavelength is sent through lens A, which makes parallel the rays of light from the source. Mirror B is a half-silvered mirror which splits the light into two beams, one going to mirror D (mirror C merely changes its direction for convenience), and the other going to mirror E. The light beams are reflected back by D and E, and are recombined at the observer's eye by means of the half-silvered mirror B. The observer sees an interference pattern of light and dark rings.

The observer notes this interference pattern, and moves mirror E along the object to be measured. For each quarter wavelength of the light source that mirror E is moved forward, the pattern changes. Light rings become dark, and dark rings become light. By knowing the wavelength of the light source, and by counting the number of pattern changes that occur, the observer can make a very accurate measure of the length moved by mirror E—the length of the object being measured.

In 1960 krypton 86 became the new standard of length. It is no longer the meter bar. The new international standard meter is 1,650,763.73 wavelengths of the orange-red light of krypton 86. With this standard and new method of measurement it is now possible to measure lengths to $\frac{1}{100,000,000}$ of an inch.

You can experiment with an interference pattern at home. Prepare two flat pieces of glass held together with rubber bands. Slip a narrow strip of paper between the glasses at the bottom. A sodium light of one wavelength is easily made. In a saucer, make a mound of three tablespoons of table salt (sodium chloride). On top of the salt pour one tablespoon of rubbing alcohol.   Light a match. Carefully set the mixture on fire, and darken the room.   In a few minutes you will see the bright yellow flame of the burning sodium.

Hold the glass on the far side of the flame.   Adjust the angle until the light of the flame is reflected to your eyes. You should be able to see an interference pattern of dark and light lines in the glass.

Some of the light is reflected back to you by the front glass and some by the rear.   Where the crests of the two waves come together, you get interference which creates bright lines.   Where the crest of one wave meets the trough of the other wave you get interference which creates dark lines.   Given the wavelength of the sodium light (about $\frac{1}{10,000}$ of an inch) and the distance between the

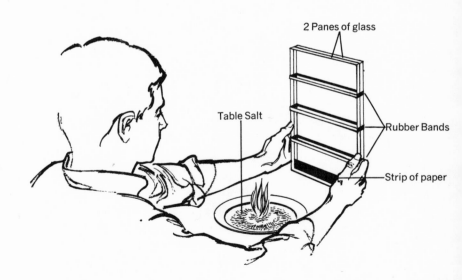

lines of the interference pattern, you could compute the distance between the two panes of glass. That distance, of course, is the measure of the thickness of the paper.

Measuring With a Laser

The krypton light, though, has one serious drawback. It can only be used to measure lengths of up to about eight inches. Beyond eight inches the interference pattern becomes indistinct, making it impossible to count the lines or rings. To measure longer distances, it is necessary to make several short measurements and add them together.

Therefore, in 1963, metrologists became very interested in the discovery of a new source of light, the laser. The name is made up of the first letters of the words light amplification by stimulated emission of radiation. The laser creates light waves of the greatest purity and intensity. Although the krypton light is quite pure, it does contain some light of different wavelengths, going off in different directions. The laser produces a light beam of a single wavelength which remains in step, crest to crest, trough to trough, for long distances.

There are several types of lasers. The laser that is used for length measurement consists of a tube filled with gas, usually a mixture of helium and neon. Encircling the tube are three electrodes. The gas gives off light when the electrodes send radio waves through the tube.

At one end of the tube, which is usually one meter long, is a mirror. At the other end is a partially silvered mirror. This mirror reflects back about 99 per cent of the light and lets about 1 per cent escape.

As the light waves are reflected back and forth from one end of the tube to the other, the atoms in the gas are stimulated or excited, so that they emit light waves, all identical in length. The small part of the light that does escape is perfectly in step. The escaping light waves are all of the same length and are traveling in the same direction.

The laser may be compared to a game of tag played by the helium and neon atoms in the tube. The radio waves pass through the tube and tag some of the atoms, causing them to emit the light. The light is then reflected back and forth in the tube tagging other atoms, causing them to emit light. The new light waves join in, tagging still other atoms. Every atom that is tagged emits light of the same wavelength. Some of the light slips out through the partial mirror producing the laser beam of just one wavelength.

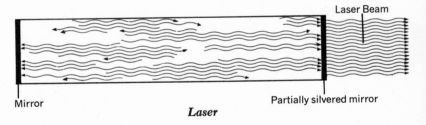

Laser Beam

Mirror

Partially silvered mirror

Laser

In 1965 a laser was used to measure a meter bar in an interferometer. With krypton, this measurement would have had to be done in five steps and the results added together. Soon, it is expected, the laser will be able to measure up to hundreds of miles with the laser beam remaining in step and producing clear interference patterns over that long distance.

There is almost no limit to the length and accuracy of measurements that will be possible with the laser beam once the few problems which remain are overcome. At the National Bureau of Standards, scientists are studying methods to keep the wavelength of the laser beams the same over periods of time, since they tend to change. When they are successful, the new standard of length may well be based on the wavelength of a laser beam. All laboratories will then be able to produce laser beams of the same known wavelength.

The laser has already been used for measuring very long distances. A pulsed laser which sends out short bursts of light, each lasting $\frac{1}{2,000}$ of a second, is used instead of a continuous beam laser as in short length measurement.

In a historic experiment in 1962, called Operation Moonbeam, a dark red beam of light from a laser was shone on the moon and a telescope was used to see the light reflected from the moon. It is known that light travels at a speed of 186,000 miles per second. By timing the round-trip of the laser pulse to the moon and back to the telescope ($2\frac{1}{2}$ seconds; $1\frac{1}{4}$ seconds each way), it was possible to calculate that the distance to the moon is about 240,000 miles.

Radar which is also used to measure the distance to the moon and the planet Venus, has confirmed these results. With radar, short radio signals are bounced off the moon and picked up by a receiver on earth. Radio waves travel at the same speed as light waves. The round trip for the radio waves was also found to be $2\frac{1}{2}$ seconds, confirming the accuracy of the laser beam.

It is of interest that the laser beam was so perfectly in step that it concentrated its circle of light on an area only two miles in diameter. The radar beam, by comparison, spread out so much that its radio signal covered a circle about 200 miles in diameter. And if there was a searchlight powerful enough to reach the moon, its light would spread out into a circle about 25,000 miles in diameter. The more the beam spreads, the less concentrated is its energy.

In the few years since its discovery, the laser has proved of immense value in many different applications. Perhaps in the near future it will become the new standard of length.

four ▪ *Mass Measurement*

ABOUT THE TIME that man first thought of ways to measure length, he also began to wonder about measuring weight. Most of the measurements needed in early times were of such light objects as jewels or gold or silver. The heavy goods were usually exchanged or bartered—a cow for a horse, a day's catch of fish for some animal skins, and so on. Early man had little need for heavy weight measurement.

As time went on, though, the range of weight measurement greatly increased, and the need for more accurate measurements also grew. Through the centuries the science of weight and mass measurement has advanced to keep pace with the demands of science and industry.

Grains to Grams

The oldest tool for comparing the heaviness of two objects dates back to about the year 7000 B.C. in Egypt. It is the *balance*. The name comes from the Latin *bi lanx*, which means two pans. At first the balance was nothing more than a straight stick hung from the branch of a tree. The Egyptians hung the stick by a string tied to its middle, so that it stayed horizontal. They placed the objects to be compared, for example, a sack of gold coins and a sack of rubies, in pans tied to both ends of the stick. If the stick remained level they knew that both sacks had the same weight. If the stick dipped to one side, they knew the sack on that side was heavier.

You can make a simple balance at home, and discover what a sensitive measuring tool it is. Insert a shirt cardboard between the pages of a thick book so that the cardboard is upright with about one inch showing. Balance a flat, wooden ruler on the cardboard. Place different light objects, such as paper clips, safety pins, thumb tacks, kernels of rice, and bits of paper on the two ends of the ruler. Compare their weights. You will be amazed to find what tiny differences you can detect with your balance.

The balance, however, does not tell how much heavier one object is compared with another. It took many years before someone had the idea of comparing objects of known weight with the object to be measured. The Egyptians chose a *grain* of wheat as the unit of weight measurement. The grain, which they took from the middle of the ear of wheat, was almost always of uniform weight.

When they placed a sack of rubies in one pan, the horizontal stick, or cross beam, tilted to that side. They added grains of wheat to the other pan to make the cross beam level once again. By counting the number of grains added to balance the beam, they knew the weight of the rubies.

The first *scale* was quite similar to the balance. But instead of two pans, it had only one. At the end of the beam without the pan the early users of the scale attached a fixed weight. They measured and notched the beam, and rested it on a sharp edge. When they placed something in

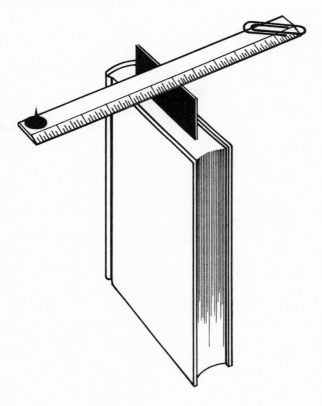

the pan, the beam tilted down on that side. Then they moved the beam so that it was resting on a point closer to the pan, and the object being weighed was balanced by the fixed weight. The balance point was read off as the weight.

The grain, one of the first units of weight measurement, is still in use today. Seven thousand grains are equal to one *pound*. Originally the pound was $1/100$ of the weight of water in a royal Egyptian cubic foot container. The

Romans divided this into 12 *ounces*, each equal to 437 grains. The English later increased the pound to 16 ounces, or a total of 6,992 grains. To make it an easier number to work with, the pound was rounded off to 7,000 grains. Thus, the modern pound is 16 ounces, each ounce equal to 437.5 grains.

For some strange reason, although pound and ounce are English words, their abbreviations are taken from the old Roman words. In Rome the pound was *libra*, and the abbreviation of pound is lb. In Rome, ounce was *onzia*, and it is abbreviated oz.

Another old weight unit which is still used today for measuring gold, diamonds, and other jewels is the *carat*. Its name comes from an Arabic bean, the *karob*. Originally, it was a weight, first equal to four grains, now to 3.086 grains. But now carat has another meaning as well. It refers to the purity of gold. Pure gold is 24-carat gold. A lower number of carats means that another metal has been added, usually to add strength to the soft gold. For example, 14-carat gold has 10 parts of another metal added to every 14 parts of gold.

Of all the units, surely the strangest is the old Chinese weight unit, the *catty*, which is also still in use today. The catty is the only unit that changes while in use! The catty begins as two full bags of rice. The coolie carrying them, though, has the right to eat as much as he needs for his meals on the way to the market. The farther the catty has to be carried, the smaller it becomes.

Weight versus Mass

The catty is the one unit of measurement that gets smaller in time. But do you know that all weight measurements change with the place they are made? At the

Equator a stone will weigh a trifle less than the same stone at the North Pole. At the top of a high mountain, a stone will weigh less than the same stone at sea level.

Why should weight change?

Weight is the pull of gravity, the gravitational force, acting on an object. The earth's gravity pulls everything toward the center of the earth. The farther away an object is, the weaker the pull of gravity on the object. The earth bulges more at the Equator than at the North Pole. Therefore the stone at the Equator is farther away from the center of the earth. The pull of gravity is weaker there, and the stone weighs less. In the same way, the stronger gravitational force on the stone at sea level makes it weigh more than the same stone acted upon by the weaker gravitational force on a mountain top.

The weight of an object is the gravitational force acting on it. The *mass* of an object is its inertia, a measure of how much it resists a change in its motion.

Imagine a pencil and a thick dictionary on a table. You want to move them both to a chair. Which object, the pencil or the dictionary, would require more effort or force to move? To put it another way, which object resists more a change in its motion?

Obviously the dictionary has more inertia and is harder to move. Therefore we know that the dictionary has greater mass than the pencil.

The inertia of an object is proportional to the amount of matter or material in the object. (It is easy to see and feel that there is more matter in the dictionary than in the pencil.) Thus another way to think of mass is as the amount of material in an object. The more material in an object, the greater its mass.

The mass of an object always stays the same unless material is either added or taken away. The number of atoms and molecules in the stone does not change, whether it is at the Equator or the North Pole, or whether it is at sea level or on a mountain top. The mass stays the same. Only the weight changes.

What would happen to your weight and mass if you were to take a rocket trip to the moon? Your mass would not change. If your mass on earth is 90 pounds, it would be the same on the moon. But the moon's gravitational force is only one-sixth as strong as the earth's. Therefore your weight on the moon would be only 15 pounds, one-sixth of your weight on earth.

People very often use the words weight and mass as **though they mean the same thing. And in most situa-** tions weight and mass are practically the same. A mass of 5 pounds has a weight of approximately 5 pounds anywhere on earth. The slight difference is not important for most purposes. But in the exacting science of metrology, every difference is significant. This constant concern for the utmost in accuracy has allowed mass measurement to develop from its primitive beginnings to its present high level.

Standard of Mass

There are four basic, primary measurements—length, mass, time, and temperature. Three of these are now based on natural standards. The standard of length, you recall, is the wavelength of the light emitted by krypton 86. The standard of time is the vibrating frequency of the cesium atom. And you will read that the standard of temperature is based on the triple point of water, the single temperature at which water can exist as a liquid, a solid, and a gas.

Only mass, of the four basic measurements, has no natural standard. The mass standard is still, as it has been since 1890, a solid metal cylinder, made of 90 per cent platinum and 10 per cent iridium, with a mass of one kilogram. And there is no active search for a standard to replace the present one.

The standard kilogram is kept in a special vault at the National Bureau of Standards. It is never touched by hand, but is always moved about with a special lifter made of ivory. When it is to be compared with another standard, two scientists are present. One takes care of the standard kilogram. The other takes care of the first scientist, making sure that nothing happens to him or to the priceless kilogram standard. And even with all this care, there is a rule at the Bureau that the kilogram may not be used more often than once a year!

The Balance

For weighing the food we buy in a market and for weighing ourselves at home we use a *scale*. In most scales the tension of a spring pulls against the gravitational force acting on the object being weighed. Therefore, most scales are measures of weight, rather than of mass.

The *balance* is the ideal tool for determining mass. In its simplest form it is a crossbeam resting on a sharp edge, from which are hung two identical pans. The scientist using the balance places the object whose mass is being measured on one pan. He places a balancing set of standard weights on the other pan. He adds or removes weights until the known mass balances the unknown object, and the crossbeam is horizontal.

Why should the balance give a measure of mass, and not

of weight? The pull of gravity is the same on both pans of the balance. When the crossbeam is not leaning toward either side, you know that both pans contain equal mass. If, for example, there is a standard kilogram mass on one pan, and the crossbeam is horizontal, then you can be sure that the other pan also contains a mass of one kilogram.

In addition to the two-pan balance, there is also a one-pan balance. Here known weights are moved along the beam to find the point of balance, which then indicates the mass of the unknown.

Mass measurements of great precision and accuracy can be made with a properly designed and used balance. The operator works the balance from a distance. Great care is taken in operating these balances, to be sure that nothing interferes with, or upsets, their functioning.

Most balances are enclosed in glass cases as a general protection against outside factors. The temperature and humidity of the room in which the balance is used do not have to be at any particular level. There is, however, great concern for the heat being radiated by the observer's body! This tiny amount of heat can throw a sensitive balance off, and produce inaccurate measurements.

Recently the National Bureau of Standards discovered that the temperature at the crossbeam is most crucial. The temperature at the pans is less important. Most of the balances at the National Bureau, therefore, have extra insulation around the upper part of the balance case.

Not only is the balance treated with great care. The weights, too, are handled most gingerly. Most standard weights are shaped to be picked up and moved easily with special lifters. This is necessary to protect the weights. It is also necessary because even so much as a fingerprint on a weight will be detected as an increase in mass by a very precise balance!

In actual use, the weights are placed in the balance several hours before the weighings are to be made. In this way the temperature and other conditions in the balance have time to stabilize. It is only then that the highly accurate and precise measurements can be made.

The balance is the great-grandfather of measuring instruments. It is over 7,000 years old, and is surrounded in measurement laboratories by many tools and instruments that are not yet 10 or 20 years old. But over the years the balance has developed into a most precise and reliable tool, which is still able to satisfy the mass measurement needs of today's most advanced science. Research, however, is already going on to find ways to improve the balance, or perhaps even to replace it, so that mass measurement can reach even higher levels.

five ▪ *Time Measurement*

A VISITOR FROM outer space would probably be amazed to see how the people on earth are controlled by the clock. A bell attached to the clock rings, and we jump out of bed. We look at it with fear, and run to catch a bus or train. We rely on it to tell us when to work and when to play. It even tells us when to eat and when to watch our favorite television show.

But, as important as the clock and time are in our lives, they are of even greater importance to the scientist. A mistake of a fraction of a second in launch time might mean that a space shot will miss its target by several miles. A delay of a millionth of a second in the return of his radio signal indicates a distance of nearly one thousand feet to the radar operator. Sending out 224 million accurately-timed electrical pulses per second makes it possible to carry up to 3,400 telephone conversations on one wire.

Calendars and Clocks

To early man, day and night, different phases of the moon, and the changing seasons were of constant concern. His observations, over many thousands of years, developed into our present system of time keeping.

The pattern of light and darkness gave man his first unit of time, the *day*.   The changes in weather showed him the four *seasons*.   The repeat of the seasons every 365 days gave man the unit of the *year*.   The calendar was devised as a way to mark off the days, seasons, and years.   It told men when to plant and when to harvest, when to expect rain and when to expect snow.

The changing appearance of the moon was also noticed. It took 29½ days from one full moon to the next.   This period became the *month*.   Twelve months equaled a year—almost.   In a calendar based only on the months, the seasons would come earlier and earlier every year.

In the year 45 B.C., Julius Caesar put into effect his famous calendar reform.   He kept the sun-based year, and changed the moon-based months.   The 365 days of the year were divided into 12 months, averaging 30½ days each.   Much later the calendar was further revised by Pope Gregory.   With some modifications, this is the calendar still in use in the Western world.

The week is not based on anything in nature, but is a man-made invention.   At first the days were named after the sun, moon, and the five known planets—Mars, Mercury, Jupiter, Venus, and Saturn.   The English, however, later substituted the names of some early gods for the names of the planets.   Thus, after Sun's day and Moon's day, came Tiw's day, Woden's day, Thor's day, Frigg's day, and Saturn's day.   From these names it was a short step to the names of today.

The first efforts to divide the day into *hours* and *minutes* dates back to about 1000 B.C. and the invention of the first instruments to measure time.   About that time, the Egyptians developed the *sun dial* to tell time by the sun's shadow. The ancient Babylonians, though, were even better time keepers. They used *water clocks*, with slowly dripping water filling a marked bowl to tell time. The modern sandfilled hour glass came from the *sand clocks*, which were also in use. Other ancient time keepers were *candles*, which marked the passage of time by the rate at which the candle grew shorter and shorter. The first *mechanical clocks*, in the fourteenth century, were gigantic and expensive pieces of equipment, suitable for use only in public places. But from them developed the clocks and watches of today.

Most of the watches and some of the clocks in your home are powered mechanically. You wind a spring, and as the spring uncoils it drives the hands of the watch or clock. Electric clocks are powered by electricity. But none of these clocks allow you to measure very, very short time intervals. A typical wrist watch ticks five times per second. The electric clock on the wall uses as its "ticks" the alternating current in the wires in your home. This current alternates, or changes direction, 60 times per second. The new electronic Accutron watch uses a tiny battery to set a tuning fork vibrating 360 times per second.

But suppose you wanted to measure some event that lasted just a small fraction of a second? Could you measure, for instance, how long it takes for you to say your name? Using the ordinary clocks or watches in your home, you could not get a very precise measurement. A clock is needed that can provide many more "ticks" in each second.

You can make your own clock to time events that last less than a second. You need only a phonograph, a protractor, and an index card or piece of paper about 3 by 5

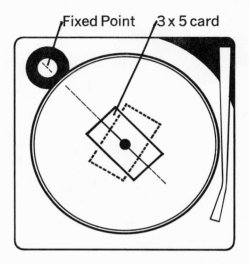

Fixed Point   3 x 5 card

inches. Hold the card with the longer side going up and down, and draw a line down the center of the card, at right angles to the shorter edge. Poke a small hole at the center of the line, and slip it on the spindle of the phonograph. Aim the line at some fixed point on the phonograph.

Hold the turntable with your hand as you click the phonograph on. Then release the turntable as you say your name, quickly grabbing it again when you finish. Keep your hand on the turntable as you click off the phonograph.

Now place your protractor on the card, with the 90° line facing the fixed point. Notice where the line on the card is now. How many degrees did the card turn as you said your name? You can now measure the time it took, depending on the speed of the phonograph:

At 78 rpm 1° = $\frac{1}{468}$ of a second
At 45 rpm 1° = $\frac{1}{270}$ of a second
At 33⅓ rpm 1° = $\frac{1}{200}$ of a second

You are able to make such accurate measurements with this equipment because it allows you to divide the second into smaller units than the usual watch or clock.

Quartz-Crystal Clocks

Nearly one hundred years ago the Curie brothers, Pierre and Jacques, discovered that when a quartz crystal is set into vibration it creates tiny bursts of electrical current. They also found that the reverse is true. If the crystal is placed in an electric current, and the direction of the current is quickly switched back and forth, the crystal is set into very rapid, very regular vibration.

A clock was built in 1927 based on a quartz crystal vibrating 100,000 times per second. This quartz-crystal clock had many thousands of times more "ticks" in each second than any other time keeper. The vibrations of the quartz created 100,000 short electrical impulses per second. These were fed into a series of frequency dividers in which the 100,000 impulses per second were reduced to 1,000 impulses per second. These impulses were then used to move the hands of a clock.

Quartz-crystal clocks are used for some of the exacting measurements done at the United States Naval Observatory. Three clocks are used so that they can be compared and any error immediately noticed. The quartz clocks are in a sealed room, with the temperature and humidity carefully controlled. The crystals themselves are enclosed in small ovens that keep them at a fixed temperature. The dials of the clocks are in a different room. No one ever enters the clock room.

At the Brookhaven National Laboratory a quartz-crystal clock is used to time the experiments run on the Cosmitron, their giant atom smasher. There is only a single clock here, but outlets throughout the building allow the scientists to "plug in" and receive the 1,000 ticks per second that emerge from the clock's frequency dividers.

Maser

One might think that with the invention of the quartz-crystal clock scientists seeking a reliable and accurate time piece would be satisfied. This time keeper divides the second very finely. While the early quartz-crystal clocks vibrated 100,000 times per second, newer ones vibrate as much as 2½ million times per second.

Yet even the quartz-crystal clock is not the perfect time keeper. As the crystal ages it loses some of its regularity and precision. It is very sensitive and it is extremely difficult to keep it vibrating at an exact frequency. Scientists had their eyes open for still another clock.

In 1948 the National Bureau of Standards developed the first atomic clock. It "ticks" billions of times per second. This clock makes use of the vibrations of the nitrogen atom within the ammonia molecule.

Each ammonia molecule contains one nitrogen atom and three hydrogen atoms. These four atoms are arranged in the form of a pyramid; the three hydrogen atoms at the three corners of the base, and the nitrogen atom at the apex. If energy, such as radio waves, is applied to the ammonia molecule, the nitrogen atom flips and jumps through the base, forming an upside-down pyramid. As

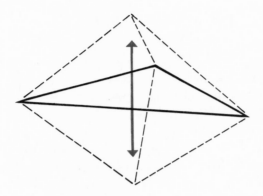

long as there is energy, the nitrogen atom will vibrate between these two positions at the rate of 23,870,000,000
times per second.

The ammonia molecules are used in a special device
called a *maser*, an acronym for microwave amplification by
the stimulated emission of radiation.   The maser contains
only excited, or high-energy ammonia molecules.   Energy, in the form of radio waves, is applied at the natural
vibrating frequency of the ammonia.   The radio waves
stimulate, or trigger, some ammonia molecules into vibrating.   They radiate energy which stimulates other molecules into vibrating, vastly amplifying the original energy.
The maser provides a strong source of energy at a very
uniform and very precise frequency.

To picture the principle of the maser, imagine an army
camped in small outposts over a large area.   The general
decides to advance.   He tells the messenger to get on the

only horse and pass the word to the camps. The messenger rides to the first outpost and tells them to advance. He gets off the horse, and one of the men from the first outpost gets on. He rides off to the next outpost and repeats the order. Then he dismounts, and a man from the second outpost gets on the horse and rides off to alert the next outpost, and so on.

Now imagine the same situation, but with a horse at each outpost. The original messenger alerts the first outpost. One of the men from the first outpost jumps on his horse, and both men ride off to warn the others. When each of them reaches an outpost, two new riders are added. Then four riders go on to the others, and so on and on.

Let us think of each outpost as an atom and each horse as energy. An atom can be either in a quiet state, without energy, or in an excited state, with energy. When energy (a horse) arrives at a quiet atom (outpost without a horse), the atom takes the energy and becomes excited. This excited atom can then send out energy and excite another atom. The first atom, though, has lost its energy, and cannot excite any others. On the other hand, when energy (a horse) arrives at an excited atom (outpost with a horse), the second atom joins the first in sending out energy. In this way, as each atom makes its contribution, the amount of energy is vastly multiplied.

In the maser, the magnets remove the ammonia molecules in the quiet state. The radio waves then stimulate the excited ammonia molecules to radiate energy, which in turn stimulates other molecules to radiate their energy. The result is a powerful source of energy at a fixed, unchanging frequency. This energy can then be used to run a clock. It can also be used to control a quartz-crystal clock, automatically adjusting the vibrating speed of the crystal if it is vibrating too fast or too slow.

The early masers used molecules of ammonia, which vibrate nearly 24 billion times per second. The more recent masers use atoms of hydrogen, which vibrate 1,420,405, 751.732 times per second. Despite the lower frequency of hydrogen, it has proved to be a steadier and more precise time keeper than ammonia.

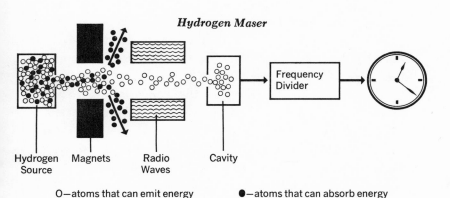

Hydrogen Maser

| Hydrogen Source | Magnets | Radio Waves | Cavity |

O—atoms that can emit energy   ●—atoms that can absorb energy

So extraordinary and exact a time keeper is the maser that even the scientific community has been taken aback at its discovery. At first some jokesters dubbed it "a solution looking for a problem." In some laboratories it is rumored that the word maser stands for money acquisition scheme for expensive research.

Scientists are hard at work finding tasks for this remarkable new time-measuring tool. One of the most important projects under study is how to use the maser to test part of Einstein's theory of relativity.

Einstein held that the flow of time is not always the same. He said that a clock moving at a constant speed runs slower than a stationary clock. But the moving clock has to be traveling at a fantastic speed before there is a significant difference between the two clocks. For instance, if the moving clock is traveling at 5½ million miles per hour, there is a 10 per cent difference in time flow. That means that when the stationary clock shows that 30 minutes have passed, the clock moving 5½ million miles per hour will show the passage of only 27 minutes.

Right now there is no way to approach speeds of millions of miles per hour. Therefore, the highly precise maser is being used to search for tiny time differences at the much lower speeds we can achieve.

Another prospect is that the vibrations of the hydrogen atom in the maser may soon become the new standard definition of a second. The Naval Observatory is exploring the possibility of using a hydrogen maser for its radionavigational system, Loran-C, and for synchronizing standard-frequency broadcasts from Naval Research Laboratories

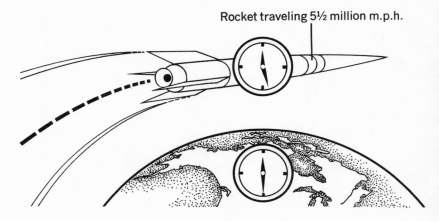

Rocket traveling 5½ million m.p.h.

throughout continental United States, Hawaii, and the Panama Canal.

Perhaps the hydrogen maser will provide evidence for a revolutionary new theory of time. At present, most of us think of time as a continuous flow. We imagine that we can divide time into intervals as small as we wish, just as we once thought that matter could be divided and subdivided without limit.

But some scientists now believe that time might be composed of particles which cannot be further divided, just as the atomic theory holds that all matter is composed of electrons, protons, and neutrons which cannot be divided. These particles of time, called *chronons*, last one-billionth of a trillionth of a second. The belief is that no event can take place in a time shorter than a chronon—the basic, indivisible unit of time.

Cesium Beam Clock

The standard of time today is the cesium beam clock, which is so accurate that it will not gain or lose more than 1 second in 30,000 years! Its billions of ticks per second are derived from cesium, a rare metallic element. The cesium beam clock depends on vibrations of the electrons within the atoms. These vibrations are entirely unaffected by any outside factors and remain remarkably stable.

Within the cesium atom are six rings of electrons orbiting around the nucleus. The outer ring contains only one electron. This single electron can be at two different angles as it spins around. When it changes from one position to the other it either emits or absorbs energy at the rate of 9,192,631,770 vibrations per second.

The cesium beam clock is usually built into a quartz-crystal clock.   Some of the vibrations from the quartz crystal are used to drive a traditional clock.   Other vibrations are stepped up to the frequency of the cesium atom. They are then changed to radio waves and focused on a long tube.   The cesium is heated to a gas and sent as a gas through the tube.

In the tube is a magnet, which removes the atoms that can emit energy, and allows through only atoms that can absorb energy.   If the quartz-crystal vibrations are precise, all the radio waves are absorbed by the cesium.   If the quartz vibrations are not exactly right, the vibrating speed of the quartz is automatically adjusted.

Cesium beam clocks are used to broadcast time signals so that clocks all over the globe will agree.   Since the speed of radio transmission varies with atmospheric conditions, however, this method does not give the precision that is desired.   Transmission by satellites has been found to be much more accurate.

In 1962 England and the United States synchronized their time standard by Telstar II, and in 1965, Japan and the United States synchronized their time via Relay II.

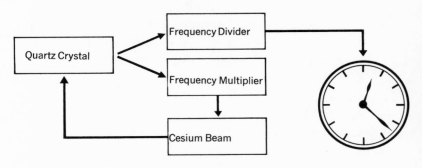

Cesium Beam Clock

Furthermore, in 1965 a portable cesium beam clock was flown from Washington, D.C. to twenty-one time-keeping stations around the world for the purpose of exact synchronization.

So accurate is the cesium beam clock that it has made it possible to detect a slight slowing down in the speed of the earth's rotation since 1962. Twice, in November, 1963, and in March, 1964, all of the world's clocks were set back one-tenth of a second so that Atomic Time (based on the cesium beam clock), would agree with Universal Time (based on astronomical observation).

Nevertheless, as wonderful as these clocks are, do not think of throwing out your clock at home. The price of the inexpensive, portable model of the cesium beam clock is still $21,600!

Dating the Past

Both the geologist with his rock samples and the archeologist with his fossils need clocks, too. But they need special clocks that are able to tell time backwards, into the past. The geologist wants to know when his rocks were formed. The archeologist wants to know how long ago his fossil was a living animal or plant. In recent years new "clocks" have been developed that allow scientists to date events anywhere from hundreds to billions of years in the past.

Around 1900, Marie Curie discovered that certain elements, which she called radioactive elements, are continually giving off rays and atomic particles. As the radioactive elements emit these rays and particles their structures change. They become different elements.

Scientists have worked out the speed at which radioactive elements decay.   It is measured in half life, which is the time it takes for half the atoms of a radioactive element to change into another element.

The half life of uranium 238, for instance, is 4½ billion years.   In that time half the atoms in a sample of uranium 238 will have changed to thorium 234.   The half life of thorium 234 is 24 days, and in that time half the atoms of thorium 234 will have changed to protoactinium 234. This process goes on until the end result is lead, which is not radioactive and does not change.

This knowledge gives us another, completely different atomic clock with which it becomes possible to date quite accurately events in the distant past.   Take the formation of the earth's crust.   The method is to find a rock that contains uranium, and measure the exact amounts of uranium and lead in the rock.   The half life figures tell us, for instance, that if the rock contained 100 pounds of uranium when it was formed, after one million years, one-quarter of an ounce of the uranium will have changed to lead. Using this approach, it has been possible to measure the ages of rocks from 50 million to 4 billion years old.   These measurements indicate that the crust of the earth was formed about 4 billion years ago, which is the probable age of the earth.

Other radioactive elements, such as carbon 14, can be used to date events that are measured in hundreds or thousands of years.   Carbon 14, a radioactive form of carbon, is part of the carbon dioxide in the air.   It can be found in all living plants and animals.   When a plant or animal dies, no more carbon 14 is taken in and the process of radioactive decay begins.

Carbon 14 has a half life of 5,760 years.   Thus, if a bone fragment is discovered and is found to be emitting half as many radioactive rays and particles as newly created carbon 14, the experimenter knows that the bone is 5,760 years old. This method is accurate to within 100 years in dating objects less than 10,000 years old.

With his new clocks man can accurately measure events that last billionths of a second, and can date events that occurred billions of years ago. He can test and question theories that are fundamental to our understanding of the universe. He is able to dwell in a world of staggering numbers and speeds. There is no limit to the possibilities that scientists will encounter in their search to conquer time.

six ▪ *Temperature Measurement*

THE TEMPERATURE FIGURES that scientists deal with today cover an amazing range—all the way from the +50 million degrees Fahrenheit of the hydrogen bomb explosion, to the −450 degrees Fahrenheit of the interstellar dust in outer space.   To be able to make precise and accurate measurements over this range, the science of temperature measurement has had to make some astounding advances over the nearly 300 years of its history.

A *Matter of Degree*

Temperature measurement developed quite late in the history of measurement.   The first *thermometer,* the instrument that measures temperature, is credited to the great scientist Galileo Galilei (1564–1642).   It was not a very satisfactory tool, though.

It is now accepted that the true founder of the science of temperature measurement is the German-Dutch instrument maker, Gabriel Daniel Fahrenheit (1688–1736).   In 1714 he invented the thermometer with a column of mercury sealed in glass.   This is still the most popular and most widely used type of thermometer.

In 1724, Fahrenheit set out to devise a temperature scale that would provide a basic unit of temperature measurement just as feet and pounds and minutes are basic to other types of measurement. He realized that to set up a temperature scale three things are needed: a fixed cold point that could always be reproduced, a similar hot point, and a division of the distance between the points into equal steps.

For his cold point, Fahrenheit plunged his thermometer into a mixture of ice and table salt. He marked this point as zero. For his hot point he chose the normal body temperature, which he called 96. (After the Fahrenheit scale was accepted it was found that the actual body temperature is 98.6 degrees.)

He divided the distance from 0 to 96 into 96 equal units, each one called one degree Fahrenheit, usually abbreviated 1° F. Almost all day-to-day temperature measurements in the United States and some other countries use the Fahrenheit scale.

Less than twenty years after Fahrenheit established the first temperature scale, Anders Celsius (1701–1744) devised the centigrade (C) scale which he considered easier to use, and more logical and scientific. He chose as his cold point the freezing point of pure water, which he called 0° C. (Fahrenheit's cold point was the freezing temperature of salt water, which is lower than the freezing temperature of pure water. The freezing temperature of salt water is 0° F or −17.7° C. The freezing temperature of pure water is 32° F or 0° C.) For his hot point, Celsius used the boiling temperature of water, which he called 100° C. He divided the distance between 0° and 100° into 100 equal parts.

In 1948 the name of the Centigrade scale was officially changed to Celsius scale (C). They are simply different names for the same thing. The Celsius scale is the temperature scale of scientists throughout the world. It is fortunate that temperature readings can be changed back and forth between the Fahrenheit and Celsius scales so simply:

$$F = \tfrac{9}{5}\,C + 32$$
$$C = \tfrac{5}{9}\,(F - 32)$$

In theory, the lowest possible point on the Celsius scale is $-273.15°$. Starting at a temperature of $0°$ C, any gas contracts and loses $1/273.16$th of its volume for each degree drop in temperature. Therefore, at $-273.15°$ C all gases should have no volume. They should just vanish! (Actually, all gases become liquid and then solid before reaching that temperature, and their rate of contraction changes.)

This temperature, $-273.15°$ C, is called absolute zero. Nothing can be at a lower temperature. At absolute zero practically all motion of molecules stops. Objects have almost no heat at all.

In 1848, the British physicist Lord Kelvin (1824–1901) proposed a temperature scale based on absolute zero. In the Kelvin scale (K), absolute zero is 0. The units are then divided according to the Celsius scale. The freezing point of pure water ($0°$ C), is $273.15°$ K, and the boiling point ($100°$ C), is 100 degrees higher, or $373.15°$ K.

At the 1948 conference, when the Celsius scale was adopted, the Kelvin scale was chosen as the standard temperature scale. The measurements, however, were to be expressed in degrees Celsius. At the 1960 conference six points were chosen as the standard reference points of temperature measurement. They are:

	Degrees Celsius
Boiling point of oxygen,	−182.97
Triple point of water	0.01
Boiling point of water	100
Boiling point of sulfur	444.60
Freezing point of silver	960.8
Freezing point of gold	1063.0

The boiling point is the temperature at which, under a pressure of one atmosphere, a liquid is in equilibrium with its vapor.   The freezing point is the temperature at which the liquid and its solid are in equilibrium.   Equilibrium exists between two phases of a substance (water and steam, water and ice, for instance), when they are in the same container, and there is no increase in either phase with the passage of time.

The triple point of water is the single temperature at which water can exist as a liquid (water), a solid (ice), and a gas (water vapor).   It is now accepted to be 0.01° C.   The triple point of water is used as the reference temperature for the most precise temperature measurement.

To find the triple point of water the scientist uses a round, hollow glass cell nearly filled with very pure water. Most of the air is removed before the cell is sealed, so there is a very low pressure.   At the center of the glass cell is a narrow well, open to the air.   The scientist drops some powdered dry ice into this well, freezing some of the water, and creating a mantle of ice around the well.   Then he fills the well with alcohol, which melts a thin layer of the ice surrounding the well.   This establishes the triple-point temperature of 0.01° C.   It is the one temperature at which water, ice, and water vapor can remain in equilibrium, with no increase or decrease in the amount of any of

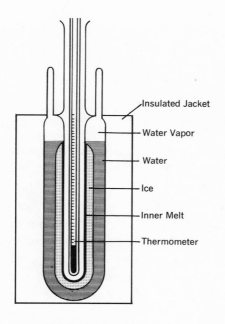

Triple Point Cell

the phases. The glass cell is kept in an insulated container to protect it from the outside temperature. A thermometer is inserted in the well to take readings on the temperature of the cell.

Once the temperature scales were established, the science of temperature measurement grew by leaps and bounds. Improved thermometers and entirely new methods of temperature measurement brought this basic measure to its present heights.

Expansion Thermometers

Expansion thermometers are based on the fact that certain materials expand with a rise in temperature. The most familiar thermometer used in the home is the *liquid-in-glass* thermometer. The liquid inside may be either mercury or colored alcohol. When the temperature of the bulb at the bottom of the thermometer is raised, the liquid expands and rises up the hollow tube. The liquid stops expanding when the temperature of the bulb is the same temperature as the object being measured. The height of the liquid in the tube shows the temperature of the bulb. The temperature can be read from the scale of degrees printed on the glass.

Another type of expansion thermometer is the *bimetallic* thermometer. It consists of two strips of different metals, usually brass and steel, joined throughout their length. Metals expand when they are heated, but different metals expand different amounts. When the two metals in the bimetallic thermometer are heated, the brass expands more than the steel. The strip, made up of both metals, then curls around, with the brass on the outside, longer curve.

Most automatic home heating systems use a bimetallic thermometer to control the temperature. The bimetallic thermometer is part of a device that is set to keep the temperature at a fixed level. This is called a *thermostat.*

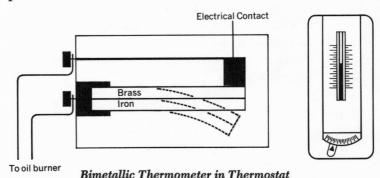

Bimetallic Thermometer in Thermostat

The bimetallic strip is placed so that when it is cold—and straight—it completes an electrical circuit which turns on the heat. The temperature of the house goes up. When it reaches a certain level the bimetallic strip curls, and breaks the circuit, turning off the heat. As the temperature drops, the strip again straightens out, completes the circuit, and starts the heat again.

Electrical Thermometers

Electrical thermometers are based on the fact that changes in temperature affect electrical characteristics. The *thermocouple* is one type of electrical thermometer in which electrical activity is used to measure temperature. It consists of two wires or strips of different metals which are joined in junctions at both ends. If the junctions are at different temperatures, a very small voltage is produced. The greater the temperature difference, the greater the voltage. For every difference of 100° C between the two junctions, a voltage of a few thousandths of a volt is produced. If the temperature of one junction is known, the voltage produced then tells the temperature difference to the other junction, which is in, or on, the thing to be measured.

One specific type of thermocouple was selected as the international standard measuring instrument in the range from 630.5° C to 1063° C. The two metals of this thermocouple are pure platinum, and an alloy of 90 per cent platinum and 10 per cent rhodium. One junction, the reference junction or cold junction, is kept in a bath of ice and pure water so that it is at a fixed temperature of 0° C. The other junction, the measuring or hot junction, is placed in, or on, the material to be measured.

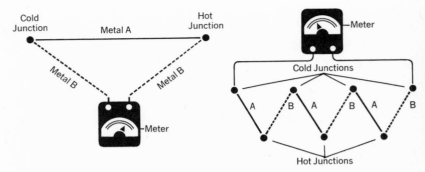

Thermocouple and Thermopile

The temperature difference produces a voltage. This voltage can be measured by a meter. The meter usually has a scale calibrated in degrees, so that the temperature can be read off easily.

A more accurate way for reading temperature measured by thermocouples is the null method. A known voltage is adjusted to equal the voltage created in the thermocouple. This balancing voltage can then be either read off in millivolts (thousandths of a volt) or translated into degrees of temperature.

When there is only a slight temperature difference between the hot and cold junctions, a very tiny voltage is produced. Sometimes the voltage is so small that it is difficult to measure, and it is helpful to increase the voltage. If several thermocouples are arranged to measure the same temperature and are connected, their voltages are added together. The total voltage is thus increased. Such a series of thermocouples is called a *thermopile*.

In most working models of thermocouples or thermopiles it is not practical to keep the cold junction at 0° C. Instead, the cold junction is kept at room temperature and is shielded from the heat of the object being measured. The meter of the thermocouple or thermopile can then be calibrated to show the degrees of temperature in this situation, or the scientist can refer to tables which provide this information.

The thermocouple is able to measure temperature because differences of temperature at the two junctions create an electrical voltage. Changes in temperature also affect the electrical resistance (opposition to flow of electrical current).

You can see the effect of a rise in temperature on resistance in this experiment. Take about one yard of bare copper wire and form it into a coil. Have a friend place a flashlight bulb against the top of a flashlight battery, holding one end of the coil of wire against the bottom of the

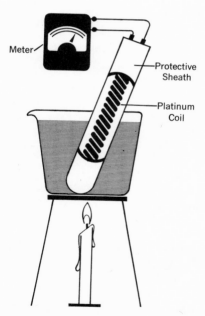

Meter

Protective Sheath

Platinum Coil

Resistance Thermometer

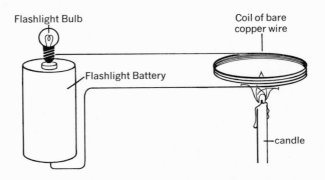

Flashlight Bulb

Coil of bare
copper wire

Flashlight Battery

candle

battery, and the other end against the side of the base of
the bulb.   The bulb will light.

Now heat the coil, either with a candle or with a match.
Watch the bulb.   You will see the light get slightly dimmer.   The rising temperature of the coil increases its resistance, allowing less electricity to flow.

The tool for measuring temperature by measuring
changes in resistance is called a *resistance thermometer*.
The resistance thermometer uses the increase in amount
of electrical resistance in a coil of wire to show rise in temperature.   As the temperature rises from 0° C to 100° C
the resistance in a platinum wire, for instance, goes up
about 40 per cent.   Thus, by measuring the increase in the
resistance of a coil of wire, the rise in temperature can be
determined.

The standard resistance thermometer consists of a coil of

thin platinum wire in a protective sheath. The platinum does not combine chemically with elements around it. It can be made very pure, and always shows the same relationship between temperature and resistance. Changes in resistance can be read directly on a meter. For more accurate results, a known resistance is balanced against the resistance thermometer. The temperature is determined by noting the resistance in the known circuit.

The resistance thermometer, which is even more reliable and precise than the thermocouple, is the standard instrument for temperature measurements between $-182.970°$ and $630.5°$ C. The thermocouple is now the standard for temperatures above $630.5°$ C. But it is expected that the resistance thermometer will soon replace the thermocouple in that range also.

Pyrometers

Have you ever described something as being "red hot" or used the expression "white heat?" Some materials, when heated to very high temperatures, do glow and give off light. The color and brightness of the light emitted change with the temperature. The tool that measures temperatures by the color of the light emitted is the *optical pyrometer.*

The optical pyrometer is a most important tool in steel mills, glass factories, and other plants where furnaces must be kept at very high temperatures. An engineer looks at the fire through an optical pyrometer to find out whether it is hot enough to melt the steel or glass or whatever material is being manufactured.

The optical pyrometer measures temperature by comparing the light of materials hot enough to be glowing,

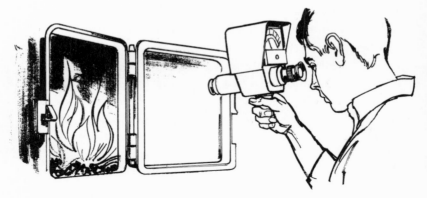

Optical Pyrometer

with the light from a glowing tungsten filament. The bulb with the filament, wider than those used in electric light bulbs, is held between the eye of the observer and the hot body to be measured. The brightness of the bulb is adjusted until the light from the tungsten filament disappears against the background of the hot body, because it is, in fact, the same color. The temperature is determined by the null method, noting the amount of current fed into the tungsten filament to make it invisible against the hot body.

You can make your own optical pyrometer. Paint stripes of dark red, bright red, orange, and yellow on a sheet of white paper. With your longest pair of pliers, hold an iron nail or pin in a flame until it begins to glow. Quickly pass the glowing nail or pin over the bands of color.

Over which color does the glow from the clip come closest to disappearing? The color tells you the temperature. Dark red is between 500° C and 600° C; bright red is between 600° C and 800° C; orange is between 800° C and 900° C; yellow is about 1000° C; and the white of the paper is close to 1200° C.

The optical pyrometer is the standard instrument for measuring very high temperatures over 1063° C. In 1961 the National Bureau of Standards developed a new and more accurate optical pyrometer. The newer instrument substitutes a photoelectric cell for the human eye. The cell produces a tiny electric current when it is struck by light. The brighter the light, the more current is produced.

The light from the hot body and from the lamp are compared by the photoelectric cell. The lamp is then adjusted so that it is exactly the same color as the hot body, as measured by the amount of current produced in the photoelectric cell. The current used by the lamp is then used as a measure of the temperature of the hot body. With the photoelectric cell temperature measurements are accurate to within $\frac{1}{50}$ of a degree in the range over 1000° C.

Still another pyrometer, the *radiation pyrometer*, may be used to measure the temperature of hot bodies above about 500° C. Instead of using visible light, though, the radiation pyrometer uses invisible heat or infrared rays given off by all bodies above absolute zero. By means of mirrors or a lens, the radiation pyrometer brings the rays to a focus. At this point there is usually a thermocouple which measures the increase in temperature.

Acoustic or Ultrasonic Thermometers

Most thermometers cannot make accurate measurements of temperatures near absolute zero. The *acoustic thermometer* or *ultrasonic thermometer* was developed to be used in this range. It is based on the fact that sound waves travel through gas at a definite speed, which depends on the temperature. The higher the temperature of the gas, the faster the speed of the sound. Therefore, measuring the speed of sound is an indirect way of measuring the temperature of the gas.

In 1965 the National Bureau of Standards adopted the acoustic or ultrasonic thermometer as the standard instrument for measuring in the range from 40° K to 14° K (−233° C to −259° C).

These new thermometers make possible research into the behavior of objects in temperatures approaching absolute zero. Take superconductivity, the ability of a very cold metal to conduct electricity without any resistance or opposition. A burst of electricity sent into a metal ring that is at a low enough temperature to be superconductive will circle the ring without resistance. It will continue to circle the ring as long as the temperature is kept down, even for years. If the temperature of the ring is raised, though, the resistance increases, and the current dies out.

The acoustic thermometer used at the National Bureau of Standards is contained within a tall upright tube that can be kept at a very low temperature. At the bottom end is a quartz crystal which provides vibrations at a known frequency. The tube is usually filled with low-pressure helium gas. At the top of the tube is a movable piston.

The piston is moved up and down. When it is a whole number of wavelengths away from the crystal, the helium is set into vibration. This causes an increase in voltage across the quartz crystal. By noting at which positions of the piston the voltage is increased, the wavelength of the sound wave can be found. Once the wavelength and the frequency are known, the speed of the sound can be found.

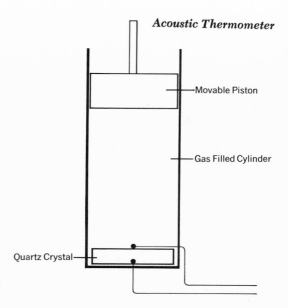

Acoustic Thermometer

Movable Piston

Gas Filled Cylinder

Quartz Crystal

And once the speed is known, the temperature of the gas can be calculated.

Calculating temperature from the speed of sound in gas is based on using a gas that has no pressure. But how is this possible? Every gas must have pressure. To get around this, measurements are made at several different pressures. They are plotted as a curve on a graph and the line is continued to give the speed at zero pressure. Once the speed at zero pressure has been determined, the exact temperature of the gas can be calculated.

Magnetic Thermometer

It may not seem possible that there is yet another thermometer that can measure even lower temperatures, but there is. To measure below 4° K scientists use the *magnetic thermometer*, the only thermometer that can measure within a few degrees of absolute zero.

There are certain chemicals, such as iron alum, which

are called paramagnetic salts. When they are at extremely low temperatures, nearly absolute zero, the spin of their ions can be made parallel to the lines of force of a powerful magnetic field. The lower their temperature, the more easily they line up. The higher their temperature, the more difficult it is to arrange them in a line. By measuring how well the spin of ions has been made parallel, the temperature can be determined.

With the magnetic thermometer, temperatures can be measured down to 0.001° K. By using even more powerful magnets and metallic ions instead of paramagnetic ions, temperatures can be measured down to 0.000001° K, the lowest temperature ever attained by man, one-millionth of a degree above absolute zero!

seven ■ *Sound Measurement*

THERE IS A FAMOUS old riddle that asks: If a tree falls in a forest, and no one is there to hear it, does the falling tree make any sound?

This riddle can be answered in two different ways, depending on how you think of sound. If you feel that sound exists only when it is heard, then you would say that the tree does not make any noise. If you feel that sound is vibration, whether or not it is heard, then you would say that the falling tree does make noise as it falls.

The two ways of thinking of sound lead to two approaches to sound measurement. In one, the units and measurements are based on how the sound is heard by people. In the other, sound measurements are made by various measuring tools. What people hear and what measuring tools hear is not always the same. In many situations sounds seem louder or softer, higher or lower to a listener than to a measuring tool.

Our ears measure the *loudness* of a sound. When a tool measures the same aspect of sound, the result is called *intensity*. Our ears measure the *pitch* of a sound, which is how high or low a sound seems to be. When a tool measures this aspect of sound, the result is called *frequency*.

Both kinds of measurements are involved in accurate

sound determinations. In building a phonograph, designing a concert hall, or making a quieter jet engine, scientists must rely both on the ways people hear the sounds, and on the precision of sound measuring instruments.

Decibels and Phons, Frequency and Mels

There is a difference in sound intensity between a shout and a whisper, between the roar of a jet and the rustle of leaves. But how can the difference be measured?

The unit used to express sound intensity is the *decibel*. It is one-tenth of a *bel*, a unit named in honor of Alexander Graham Bell. The decibel is not a direct unit. Rather it is a ratio of intensity between one sound and another.

In 1935 and 1936 the United States government tested 5,000 people—10,000 normal ears. They found the very softest sound, vibrating with a frequency of 1,000 vibrations per second, that half the people could hear and half could not. This sound became the reference for sound intensity measurements.

A sound of the same intensity as the reference sound has a level of zero decibels. A sound that is 10 times more intense has a level of 10 decibels. A sound 100 times more intense has a level of 20 decibels. And so on. For every 100 times more intense a sound is, the decibels increase by 10.

Sound intensity, then, is measured as the ratio between the reference sound and the sound being measured. This idea of using a ratio to express sound intensity came from the effort to find the smallest difference in sound intensity that a person could distinguish. It is as though there are ten people seated in a room. If one more enters, you easily notice the difference. But if there are 100 people in a room and one enters, you do not notice one more. You would be aware, however, if ten more people enter.

It is not the number of people that come in that is important. Rather it is the ratio of people entering to the number of people already there—10 per cent in our example—that determines whether you notice the difference or not.

The decibel ratings of many familiar sounds have been found. The sound of rustling leaves is about 20 decibels, quiet conversation is 40 decibels, the sound level of a busy department store is 60 decibels, inside a subway train the intensity is about 100 decibels, and 20 feet away from a jet airplane motor is 115 decibels. Any sound above 120 decibels is experienced as a tickling sensation or pain by the human ear, and not as sound at all.

The unit used to express the loudness of a sound as it is heard by the human ear is the *phon*. The loudness of a sound depends on its intensity. It also depends on the frequency of vibration of the sound. To measure loudness, therefore, you have to know both the intensity of the sound and its frequency.

The phon is the loudness level of a sound of any frequency that sounds as loud as a reference sound at 1,000 vibrations per second. In general, the lower the frequency of the sound, the greater the intensity needed for it to be as loud. (The baritone must sing with more intensity to sound as loud as the soprano; the tuba must play with more intensity to sound as loud as the trumpet.) A sound of 100 vibrations per second must have an intensity of 50 decibels to seem as loud as a sound of 1,000 vibrations at a level of 20 decibels. The 50 decibel sound at 100 vibrations per second, therefore, has a loudness level of 20 phons. A 20 decibel sound vibrating 1,000 times per second will have the same number of phons.

All sound is vibration, and fundamental to sound measurement is a measure of the vibrating speed of sound waves. The *frequency* is the measure used, and the results are expressed as vibrations per second.

Just as loudness is related to intensity, so pitch is related to frequency. The unit of pitch is the *mel.* Pitch is how high or low a note sounds to the listener. It is determined by the frequency of sound vibrations.

To establish this unit, large numbers of listeners were tested. They were asked to match different frequencies at the same intensity. They were asked to distinguish higher and lower frequencies. In one test the listeners were asked to adjust a given tone to one-half the frequency of a tone of 5,000 vibrations per second. Surprisingly enough, the average listener adjusted the given tone to less than 2,000 vibrations per second, instead of the expected 2,500 vibrations per second.

On the basis of these tests and many others, the mel scale of pitch was established. A tone vibrating at a frequency of 1,000 vibrations per second is said to have a pitch of 1,000 mels.

For the lowest audible pitches, the actual frequency is higher than the pitch in mels. By the frequency of 200, the mel scale is higher; 200 on the frequency scale is equal to 300 mels. By 1,000 the frequency and the mels are the same. Above 1,000 the frequencies rise much faster. The frequency of 1,900 equals 1,500 mels, the frequency of 4,000 equals 2,250 mels, and the frequency of 14,000 equals only 3,250 mels.

Microphone

Sound measurements are based on the fact that all sound is energy. But it is difficult to measure this form of en-

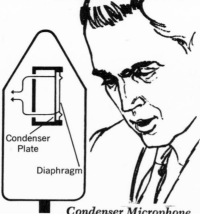

Condenser
Plate

Diaphragm

Condenser Microphone

ergy. Almost all sound measurements, therefore, are made by changing the varying patterns of sound intensity and frequency into varying patterns of electrical energy. The tool which is able to do this is the *microphone.*

Microphones, contrary to popular belief, do not make sounds louder. When a performer sings into a microphone, the microphone changes the sounds into patterns of electrical current. This current from the microphone is built up in an amplifier and then fed into a loudspeaker. The loudspeaker changes the electrical current back into sound which is louder than the sound that was received by the microphone.

The microphone can be compared to an imaginary machine gun that can shoot bullets at any speed and of any size. High pitched sounds, sounds which are vibrating at high frequencies, send out bursts of current (bullets) very

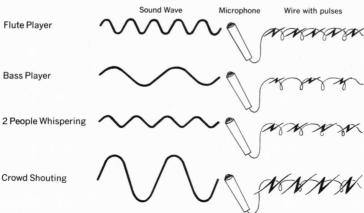

	Sound Wave	Microphone	Wire with pulses
Flute Player			
Bass Player			
2 People Whispering			
Crowd Shouting			

quickly.   Low pitched sounds vibrating at lower frequencies, send out fewer bursts of current.   A tone with a frequency of 1,000 vibrations per second, for example, will send out 1,000 bursts of electrical current every second. A lower tone, with a frequency of 500 vibrations per second, will send out only 500 bursts per second.

More intense, or louder, sounds send out more current in each burst (bigger bullets); less intense, or softer, sounds send out less current in each burst.   Thus, in all microphones, the pitch or frequency of the sound determines how often a burst of current is sent out.   The loudness or intensity of the sound determines how much current will flow in each burst.

The *condenser microphone* is the most desirable of the several types of microphones used for sound measurements.   This microphone is built around a condenser which consists of two metal plates next to each other but not touching.   The front one is a thin, flexible metal plate, called the diaphragm.   The back plate is a fixed, unmoving plate, which is given a positive electrical charge, opposite to the negative charge on the diaphragm.

When sounds strike the diaphragm they make the diaphragm bend and vibrate.   As the diaphragm moves back and forth in relation to the fixed plate, a varying electric current flows in the microphone circuit.   The higher the frequency of vibration, the more often the diaphragm moves toward the fixed plate, and the more frequent are the bursts of current.   The more intense the sound, the closer the diaphragm moves to the plate, and the greater the amount of current in each burst.

Different types of microphones are used for different measuring tasks.   Each of the microphones has its own strengths and weaknesses.   The choice of microphone depends on which one will create electrical current most directly proportional to the sound energy being measured. Once the microphone has changed the sound energy into electrical energy, electrical measurements can be made on the current produced by the microphone.

Meters

Sound intensity measurements are made with a *sound level meter.* All meters have a microphone which receives the sounds being measured and changes them into patterns of electrical current. An amplifier increases the electrical current proportionally. The amplified current is then fed into a meter which either can show the electrical current, or can be calibrated to indicate decibels. Sometimes the current is fed into a computer or other recording device, and a permanent record of the measurements is made.

Somewhat similar to the sound level meter is the *VU meter,* which is a practical tool designed to measure the loudness, or volume, in sound transmission and recording. It is used by all broadcast, recording, and telephone engineers. It is an easy way to measure the loudness level of music or speech, so that it can be kept at a comfortable level, loud enough to be easily heard, but not loud enough to distort the sound.

If you have recorded with one of the better tape recorders you have probably used a VU meter. The term VU stands for volume units, which are units of loudness especially devised for use in this meter. The VU meter does not show decibels.

The *audiometer* is a loudness measuring tool. It compares your hearing with normal standards. The audiometer produces sounds of controlled frequency at controlled intensity levels. Any loss of hearing can be determined by noting at what frequencies and intensities the audiometer sounds are audible or inaudible to the person being tested. This tells the doctor how to help a person with hearing difficulties.

The tools used to measure sound frequency are called *frequency analyzers*. The first part contains a microphone which changes frequency of sound vibration into frequency of electrical vibration. Then there are several arrangements of electronic circuits to count the number of electrical impulses being received every second. In some cases the frequency is compared with a standard frequency, such as an electrically vibrating tuning fork, or with the standard frequency radio broadcasts of the National Bureau of Standards.

Cathode Ray Oscilloscope

The *cathode ray oscilloscope* is a favorite tool for sound measurement because it is able to make visible pictures of the invisible sound waves. The scope, as it is called, changes vibrations into electrical voltage.

This instrument is built around a tube very similar to the picture tube of your television set. At the narrow end is a metal filament or cathode. When the cathode is heated, a positively charged anode plate in front of it pulls a stream of electrons from the cathode. The electrons fly through a narrow hole in the anode, and form a thin beam of electrons which passes through the entire length of the tube.

There are four metal plates, above and below and on both sides of the electron beam. They are able to control the direction and movement of the beam. The pair of plates on the two sides of the beam can make it go back and forth in the horizontal direction across the face of the tube.

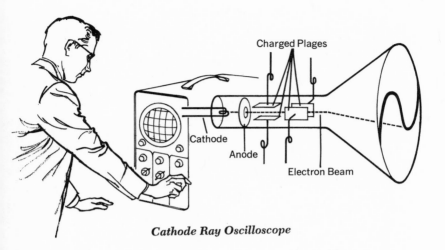

Cathode Ray Oscilloscope

Usually these plates are connected to a circuit that sends the beam across the screen at a set speed, and then has it jump back and cross again, over and over.

The pair of plates above and below the beam can make it go up and down. Usually the varying voltage from the microphone used in sound measurement experiments is fed into these plates, causing the beam to go up and down. The more intense the sound, the higher and lower the beam will go. The greater the frequency, the more often it will go up and down.

By using both sets of plates, the electron beam is made to trace a curve across the face of the tube. Since the large end of the tube is covered with a fluorescent chemical that glows when struck by electrons, the metrologist can actually see the sound waves. The intensity of the sound determines the height of the wave. The frequency determines how many waves will appear in each sweep across the tube.

The scope can measure frequency in another way.   The frequency to be measured is fed into one set of plates, and a standard reference frequency is fed into the other.   The two frequencies, working at right angles to each other, then create certain geometric figures which show their relationship.   Here are some of the figures formed and the relation of known frequency to unknown:

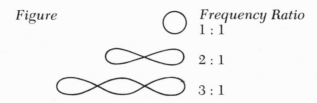

Figure	*Frequency Ratio*
◯	1 : 1
⧖	2 : 1
⧖⧖	3 : 1

The line of sound wave traced by the scope is seldom a simple curve.   Just one note played by a violin, for instance, will show many different frequencies.   If the string is vibrating 220 times per second we hear the note A.   But at the same time parts of the string are vibrating 440 times per second, 660 times per second, 880 times per second, and so on.

The sounds created by these faster vibrations are called overtones.   They blend in with the basic note and are not heard separately.   But they give the note its own tone quality or color.

Each sound source has its own pattern of overtones. One source may bring out the low overtones, but not the high ones.   Another, quite the opposite, may have no low overtones but very strong high ones.   Still others may have few overtones of any kind.   Thus, a violin A sounds different from a sung A, which is different from the same A played on a flute, trumpet, or piano.   Although each one is at the same frequency, each one has

Trumpet

Flute

Saxophone

Violin

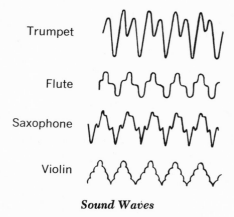

Sound Waves

a different pattern of overtones, and as a result, a different tone quality.

The scope is useful in presenting a picture of the sound wave which shows all the frequencies, with the frequencies of the overtones added to the frequency of the fundamental note. By analyzing the curve traced on the scope, it is possible to find the various overtones in a sound, and thereby measure the tone quality.

Other Sound Measurements

The speed of sound as it travels through a particular solid, liquid, or gas is a frequent subject of measurement. Sound of any frequency travels through air at room temperature with about a velocity of 1,100 feet per second, a little less than ⅕ mile per second. Sound travels much faster through water, nearly one mile per second. And in a solid like iron it travels faster yet, over three miles per second.

Once you know the speed of sound through air, you can

measure the distance to a bolt of lightning during a storm. Lightning and thunder come from the same place at the same time. Light travels 186,000 miles per second, so you see the lightning almost immediately. Sound travels through air at ⅕ mile per second. The number of seconds from the time you see the lightning until you hear the thunder, multiplied by ⅕ mile, is the distance to the lightning.

For experimental measurements of the speed of sound through a gas or liquid the *acoustic interferometer* is often used. It may surprise you to learn that this instrument is the same as the acoustic thermometer used for measuring temperatures near absolute zero.

The acoustic interferometer works this way. The metrologist fills a tube with the gas or liquid he is studying. He sets the quartz crystal at the bottom end into vibration by applying an electrical current. He seals the top of the tube with a piston that can be moved up and down.

As he moves the piston, there are points when it is a whole number of wavelengths away from the vibrating crystal. At these points the gas or liquid is set into vibration. When this happens, there are sudden increases in the voltage on the crystal. By noting the positions of the piston, the metrologist can find the wavelength of the sound. If he multiplies the wavelength by the vibrating frequency of the crystal, he gets the velocity of sound through that particular gas or liquid.

Sound waves as they hit different materials and surfaces behave in different ways. Some materials take in or absorb the sound. Other materials bounce the sound around and make it even louder.

Clap two spoons together in the living room of your

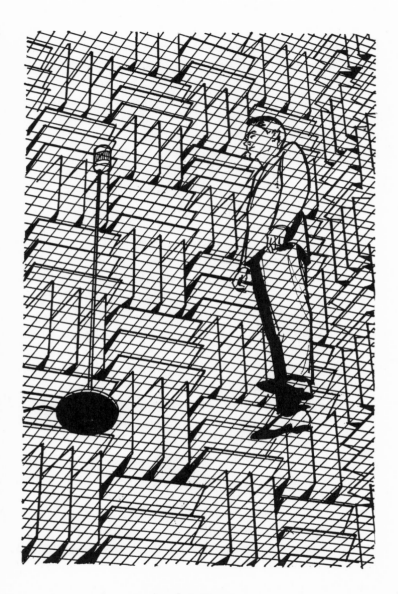

Anechoic Room

home. Notice the sound they make. Then clap the spoons deep inside a full clothing closet. Here the sound is much softer because the clothes absorb much of the sound. Clap the spoons, once again, in the bathroom. The sound here, most likely, is louder. The hard surfaces found in most bathrooms bounce, or reflect, the sound back and forth making it even louder.

When a sound is reflected and continues to ring after it is made, it is called *reverberation*. Reverberation is measured as the time it takes for a sound to drop 60 decibels from its original level.

At the Bell Telephone Laboratories in Murray Hill, New Jersey, there is a room where 99.98 per cent of all reverberation is removed. It is an anechoic room, a room without echo.

The room has 24-inch masonry walls, and is 38 by 45 feet large, with 38-foot-high ceilings. The four walls, floor, and ceiling are lined with 5-foot-long wedges of fiberglass to absorb all sound waves. Scientists and their tools stand on a grill of metal wire over the floor. In this room the most highly accurate measurements can be made without the interference of outside noises, and without reverberations of the sound itself.

There have been some impressive developments in the science of sound within the last few years—from better sound production on hi-fi records and phonographs to more natural sounding telephones, from quieter schools and factories to less annoying jet engines, from more reliable diagnosis of ear diseases to better hearing aids. These accomplishments in the field of acoustics, the science of sound, depend on the advances made in the field of modern sound measurement.

eight ■ *Light Measurement*

Light is very important to us. From the blinding glare of the sun to the faint glow in a dark theater, we are surrounded by light and color. Without light, we could not see; without light, objects would have no color; and without light, green plants would not be able to grow. In fact, our very existence depends on light.

Since man first learned to use light from a fire or candle, he has found more and more uses for light. Scientists, for instance, use natural light from the stars to see into outer space through a telescope. They use artificial light to see microscopic life through a microscope. They use light from the sun to power space shots. They use the light from krypton 86 as the standard of length measurement. They use light from glowing materials to measure temperature in the optical pyrometer. The astronomers, the biologists, the space scientists, the metrologists—and many other scientists as well—depend on light in their research. And as science advances, so does the need for accurate and reliable measurements of light.

Candles, Candelas, Lumens, and Lux

The early unit of light measurement was the *candle*. It was the intensity of light from the flame of a sperm-oil candle, one inch in diameter. Over the years, though, the flickering candle flame was found to be too uncertain a standard for light measurement. Other flame standards were tried. Several metals heated to glowing were also studied. None had the reliability and uniformity and precision that were needed.

In 1931 the National Bureau of Standards accepted a new platinum standard that had been suggested by workers in their laboratories. Platinum that is heated to its melting point (2042° K), produces a yellow-white light. The platinum is first melted and then allowed to become solid. The light produced when it becomes a solid is always the same in intensity.

With the platinum standard came a new unit of light intensity, the *candela*. The platinum standard is said to have an intensity of 60 candelas per square centimeter. One candela, therefore, is one-sixtieth as intense as the platinum standard. Since the platinum standard is very difficult to prepare and use, most day-to-day measurements are done with special electric lamps. These lamps are calibrated to the platinum standard.

Another unit of light is the *lumen*. It is the standard of the rate of light flow, or flux. A light which emits one candela in all directions, emits about 12½ lumens. The rating of a lamp should really be expressed in lumens. Household lamps, however, are usually rated in watts, which indicate the power consumed, but not the light output.

The usual 50-watt frosted incandescent lamp, such as you use at home, has an output of about 660 lumens; a 75-watt lamp produces 1,100 lumens; a 100-watt lamp, 1,650 lumens. The number of lumens produced in lamps depends not only on the wattage.   It also depends on how long the lamp is designed to burn.   Long-life lamps produce less light for the same power as the usual lamps. Photoflood lamps produce the maximum light output. But they are designed to burn for a total of only six hours.

A very important unit of light is the *illumination*, or amount of light falling on a surface, such as a book, a table, or a road.   The most widely used unit of illumination is the *foot-candle*, which is lumens per square foot.   It is the illumination cast by a source of one candela intensity at a distance of one foot.   You need about 15 foot-candles of illumination on the page for comfortable reading.   Night baseball games require about 30 foot-candles on the playing field.   A watchmaker should have 100 foot-candles on his bench.

Normal street lighting gives about $\frac{1}{20}$ of a foot-candle. Bright moonlight is $\frac{1}{40}$ of a foot-candle.   The light from the noonday sun, however, measures about 10,000 foot-candles!   The illumination unit in the metric system is the *lux*, which is lumens per square meter.   One foot-candle equals 10.76 lux.

Visual Photometry

The science of measuring light is called photometry. One approach to photometry, visual photometry, uses the eye to judge the intensity of light, and the tool which is used is the *visual photometer.*

When using a visual photometer, the scientist allows light from an unknown source to fall on a screen alongside, but shielded from, light from a known standard.   He then moves the screen between the two sources until both lights appear to provide the same illumination on the surface. The position of the screen indicates the intensity of the unknown source as compared to the standard. The eye is quite sensitive in its ability to match the two light sources, as long as they are the same color.

You can make a simple visual photometer out of a shoebox. In the center of the two ends and in the center of one long side, draw one-inch circles with a compass. Cut out these three circles. Fold an 8½- by 11-inch piece of white typing paper in half along the length, and without opening the paper, fold it in thirds across the width. Tape the two shorter edges of the paper together with the tape on the inside. The paper is now in the shape of a triangle. Arrange the triangle inside the box so that one up-and-down fold appears exactly at the center of the hole on the long side of the box. Tape the triangle to the back of the box and put the cover on.

Suppose you want to use your visual photometer to compare the intensity of the light from two flashlights. Darken the room and position the flashlights on books so that light from each one enters the box through the end holes. (The experiment will work best if the reflectors can

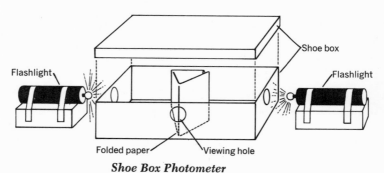

Flashlight

Shoe box

Flashlight

Folded paper Viewing hole

Shoe Box Photometer

be removed from the flashlights.)   Look through the hole on the long side and observe the light striking two of the faces of the triangle.

Are the two sides of the triangle equally bright?   If not, which side is brighter?   Move the box slowly toward the dimmer side until both sides of the paper triangle appear equally bright.   When both sides are balanced, measure the distance from the center of the box to the lamp of each flashlight.   The light from the flashlight that is farther away is more intense than that from the closer flashlight.

A basic law of light measurement, the inverse-square law, is that the amount of light striking a surface decreases by the square of the distance to the light source.   For example, a lamp two feet away from a surface must be four (2 times 2) times as bright as a lamp one foot away to provide the same illumination.

You can test this law with your visual photometer. Take a long, thick candle and cut it into five short candles.   Be sure that the candles are tall enough so that their light enters the end holes of the box and falls on the viewing triangle.

Place four of these short candles at one end of the box, two feet away from the center, and one candle at the other end two feet away from the center.   Darken the room and look through the hole on the long side.   You will see that the side of the triangle lighted by the four candles appears very much brighter than the side lighted by one candle— actually four times brighter.

Now carefully slide the single candle toward the box until the illumination on both sides of the triangle appears to be equal.   Measure the distance from the candle to the center of the box.   How much did it measure?   About one foot? The illumination from a candle one foot away is four times as great as from a candle two feet away. Therefore, one candle, one foot away, should provide the same illumination as four candles, two feet away.

If you have enough candles you might like to see how far away you would have to place a single candle to balance nine candles that are three feet away. The illumination from one candle, one foot away, equals the illumination from nine candles (three squared) three feet away.

Your shoebox photometer works on the same principle as the visual photometers in science laboratories. In actual use, the scientist places a known standard source of light at one end of a metal bench with distances marked along the edge. He places the unknown light source at the other end of the bench. At the center he puts the photometer head, a device consisting of mirrors and prisms and a surface that allows him to see light from both sources side by side with a very fine dividing line. Usually the light from one source appears in the shape of a semicircular disk, with the light from the other source forming the other half of the circle.

He moves the photometer head along the bench toward one source or the other until the two halves of the photometer field appear equally bright. Knowing the intensity of the standard source, and noting the position of the photometer head, he applies the inverse-square law relating illumination and distance to get a very accurate measure of the intensity of the unknown source.

Physical Photometry

Visual photometry depends on the trained eye of an experienced observer to obtain accurate results. But it is quite slow, and the precision is not very high.   The needs of modern science demand high speed of operation and great precision.

The more modern approach to photometry, physical photometry, is to use a physical measuring instrument instead of the eye.   The basic detector used in physical photometry is the photoelectric cell or *phototube*, with special filters so that its sensitivity resembles that of the eye.

Have you ever approached a door that opened before you reached it, or have you dried your hands under a hot-air drier that started when you put your hands under it? If so, then you have probably encountered a phototube. Both of these bits of scientific "magic" work with what is popularly called an electric eye.   It is really a phototube.

For more than a hundred years, we have known that certain metals emit electrons when they are exposed to light. This effect is the basis of the phototube.   Enclosed in a

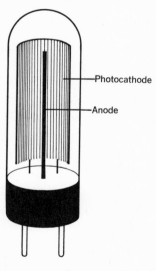

Photocathode

Anode

Phototube

sealed, evacuated glass tube is a plate coated with a thin layer of a metal, such as selenium or cesium.   These metals are specially chosen because they emit electrons readily when exposed to light.   This plate is called the photocathode or cathode.   In front of the cathode is a thin rod or a wire mesh, called the anode.   The anode has a positive electric charge, obtained from a battery or other source of direct current.

When light falls on the cathode, electrons are emitted and are attracted to the positively charged anode, causing a flow of electricity.   When there is light, there is current; when there is no light, there is no current.

Automatic doors and hand driers are arranged so that a beam of light shines directly on the phototube at all times. As long as the light strikes the phototube, electricity flows, and the door remains shut or the drier remains off. But when you block the light, the electricity stops flowing, signaling the door to open or the drier to blow.

Photometers which use phototubes come in many different shapes and sizes, depending on their use.   In each one, though, the light to be measured falls on the photocathode, thereby releasing electrons.   The electrons are attracted to the positively charged anode, resulting in a flow of electricity that can be measured with a sensitive meter.   The greater the amount of light striking the phototube, the greater the current.   The size of the electrical current is directly proportional to the amount of light striking the photocathode.

Some photodetectors, operating on another principle, are called *barrier-layer* cells.   They are also called *photovoltaic cells* because they generate a voltage and do not require a battery for operation.   The current generated depends on the intensity of the light which strikes the cell. The barrier-layer cell is arranged in layers, like a sandwich. On the bottom is an iron plate. The middle layer is a metal such as selenium, which emits electrons when illuminated. On top of the selenium is a very thin transparent metal layer that serves as a conductor for the emitted electrons. When light strikes the barrier-layer cell, current flows through the selenium to the base plate. The current can be measured with a meter, and is approximately proportional to the intensity of the light striking the cell.

You have used a barrier-layer cell if you have used a light meter for determining exposures in photography. For this purpose, the current that is produced operates a meter. The meter is usually calibrated to indicate directly the correct shutter speed and lens opening for the available light.

Both the phototube and the barrier-layer cell change the energy of light into electrical energy that is directly proportional to the light energy. With these tools, precise light measurements can be made on the intensities of light sources, ranging from a tiny electric light bulb to the noonday sun.

Visual Colorimetry

Just as photometry is a measure of the intensity, rate of flow, and illumination of light, so colorimetry deals with the measurement of color, another important aspect of light.

Both the artist and the scientist interested in colorimetry think of colors in the order in which they appear in a rainbow or spectrum—red, orange, yellow, green, blue, indigo, and violet. To the artist, each color has a special mood or feeling.   To the scientist, though, each color is a vibrating beam of light, and the different colors are the results of combinations of different wavelengths.

The shortest light waves are violet in color, with a length of about $\frac{1}{60,000}$ of an inch.   The longest light waves are red, with a length of just under $\frac{1}{30,000}$ of an inch.   From the violet to the red side of the rainbow, each of the colors has a longer wavelength than the one before.

The painter and the scientist agree that each color has three qualities, though they often disagree on their names. The scientist refers to a particular color of the rainbow —red, blue, yellow, green, and so on—as the hue; brightness or value describes the color on a scale running from dark to light; and chroma or saturation places the color on a scale that runs from weak to vivid.

The American painter Albert H. Munsell (1858–1918) devised what he called a color tree in an effort to introduce some order into the use and understanding of color and color terminology.   The central trunk of the color tree is a thin column that shows the scale of brightness, or value, from black to white.   Arranged radially around the trunk are the hues—red, orange, yellow, and so on.   Any branch shows the chroma, or saturation, of a color, going from very weak at the trunk to very strong at the end.   By assigning each color a Munsell notation, it is possible to express color appearance by number.

The colors, as on the Munsell color tree, may also appear in color dictionaries, such as Maerz and Paul's *Dictionary of Color*.   This book contains 7,056 different color samples, along with 4,000 of the most popular names for these colors.

Colorimetry, like photometry, uses both visual and physical methods of measurement. *Visual colorimetry* uses the eye to match the unknown color to a known color such as on the Munsell scales. Sometimes this is done by directly comparing color samples until a match is found. Other times the unknown color is found by mixing together varying amounts of red, blue, and green light. Any color can be duplicated by combining the right proportions of these colored lights. The unknown color is then defined by the proportions of each of the three colored lights that were used.

It is accepted that physical photometry gives more accurate and more reliable results than visual photometry for most measurements. A phototube is a better judge of brightness than the eye. The situation is somewhat different, however, in colorimetry. There are strong psychological factors which affect the appearance of colors. Therefore, visual colorimetry will very often give more meaningful results than the best physical colorimeter.

You have probably experienced the "tricks" that colors can play on you. When you buy clothes have you noticed how some colors make you seem stout and other colors make you seem slim? Tests have shown that perfectly good food served under green light will make people ill. The very same food served under yellow or reddish light, looks tempting and tastes delicious.

To see how colors influence each other, take a few pieces of colored construction paper. Look at a piece of green paper. Then take a piece of red paper, cut a large hole in the center, and place it over the green. Do you see how the green appears a stronger color? Now put a yellow paper with a hole over the green. You will notice that the green seems bluer now. Blue around a gray or white spot makes it seem yellow.   White around any color makes the color within appear darker.

In October, 1967, the National Bureau of Standards reported the results of a two-year study on the effects of surrounding colors on a target color.   The result is a series of equations that make it possible to predict the appearance of any color when surrounded by any other color or colors.

Physical Colorimetry

Physical colorimetry is based on the fact that a surface of any color reflects light of just that color—a red surface reflects red light, a blue surface reflects blue light, and so on. If lights of the same intensity, but different color, are shined one at a time on a surface, the color that is reflected most intensely is the same color as the surface.

The instrument of physical colorimetry is the *spectrophotometer.*   This tool breaks white light, which contains all colors, into a spectrum of individual colors by means of either a prism or a diffraction grating.   A movable narrow slit allows a light beam of only a narrow wavelength band, or one color, to pass.   This beam falls on the color sample being tested.   Another beam falls on a disk coated with a standard white reflector, such as magnesium oxide.

Both the sample and the standard are placed at holes in

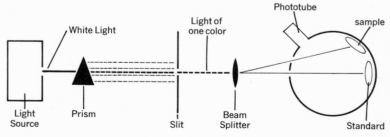

Spectrophotometer

the wall of a hollow white sphere, called an integrating sphere.   At a window in the sphere is a phototube which measures the intensity of the light being reflected from the sample and from the standard.

The two beams are controlled so that while the maximum light is on the sample, there is minimum light on the standard.   Then they are reversed, minimum on the sample, and maximum on the standard.   The phototube is attached to equipment that keeps a record of the intensity of reflection from the sample and the standard, with light of one particular color.

Then the slit is moved so that light of a different wavelength band is sent into the integrating sphere, and another record is made of the light reflected.   This is done with perhaps 30 different colors of the spectrum, noting the intensity of the reflected light with each color.   From these results the actual color of the sample can be computed.

This procedure is used to determine the color of opaque samples.   The spectrophotometer, however, can also be used to find the color of transparent materials, such as liquids, gases, glass, or plastic.   In this application the narrow wavelength bands are sent through the unknown material.   By noting how much light of each wavelength band is absorbed by the unknown sample, its color can be determined.

One of the many valuable uses for the spectrophotometer is in analyzing biological and chemical samples. Small amounts of different substances in samples can be identified and measured by color, by how they affect the reflection or transmission of light.   There are many different spectrophotometers that can be used to make measurements from a tiny trace of a chemical in blood, to the exact color of a chip of paint, to the kind and amount of pollution in a sample of air.

Speed of Light

Surely the most famous equation in all science is $E = MC^2$. This amazing equation, first stated by Albert Einstein (1879–1955) in 1905, holds that mass can be changed into energy; E, energy, is equal to M, mass, times C^2, the speed of light squared. The entire science of atomic energy is based on this little equation. And the equation itself is based on the constant C, the speed of light in a vacuum.

The first modern measurements of the speed of light were made by the American astronomer and physicist Albert Abraham Michelson (1852–1931). In a famous experiment he placed mirrors on Mt. Wilson and Mt. San Antonio, two mountains in California that are 22 miles apart.

One evening in 1926, he sent a narrow beam of light through a slit and on to one face of a rotating, eight-sided mirror. From there, by a series of mirrors, he reflected the light from Mt. Wilson, across to the mirror on Mt. San Antonio, and back to the rotating mirror.

Michelson was able to control the rotating speed of the mirror. At most speeds the image he saw was blurred and dim. Only at one speed, exactly 528 rotations per second, did the reflected beam of light return at the same instant as the next face of the mirror replaced the one facing Michelson. On this basis, he was able to compute the speed of light as 186,285 miles per second through air.

Michelson later repeated the experiment in a one-mile

long, airtight tunnel, so that he could measure the speed of light in a vacuum.

Since then many experimenters have measured the speed of light by measuring the speed of radio waves, which are longer than light waves, but which travel at the same speed in a vacuum. In most experiments the results have only confirmed Michelson's early findings. The speed is now accepted to be 186,284 miles per second, with no more than 2½ miles per second error in either direction.

On the basis of Einstein's special theory of relativity, it is now believed that nothing in the world can move faster than the speed of light. In the future we can expect more and more tests of this theory, and more and more careful measurements of the speed of light which is at the heart of this theory.

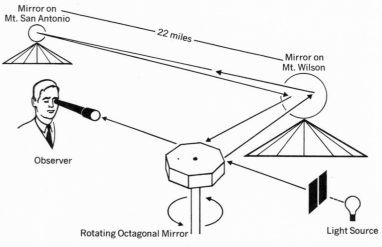

Speed of Light Experiment

nine ■ *Electrical Measurement*

On May 12, 1966, a strange looking procession left Washington, D.C., heading northwest. A police escort was in the lead, followed by a very ordinary station wagon. The station wagon carried no famous public figure, no priceless work of art, not even a shipment of gold or money. Rather, seated in the car were several scientists from the National Bureau of Standards guarding an ordinary metal box.

Why a police escort for a simple little box? Because the box contained a group of the Bureau's voltage cells, one of the standards of electrical measurements for the entire United States. If the sensitive cells were to be shaken, jolted, tipped, or exposed to the light, they would be ruined. Research and production in the fields of electronics, aerospace, and communications would be hampered for years to come. The National Bureau of Standards was moving from its old buildings in Washington, D.C., to its new laboratories at Gaithersburg, Maryland. And one of the most delicate tasks of the move was the transfer of the voltage cells.

After driving some twenty miles, the motorcade stopped at the new location of the National Bureau of Standards. Most gingerly the box was carried inside by hand. In fifteen separate trips the remaining voltage cells were brought over.

After several months of testing it was found that the voltage standards had indeed survived the trips and were functioning well in their new home. Along with the voltage cells, the various other standards and tools of electrical measurement were transferred with equal success.

Amperes, Volts, and Ohms

Electricity, as you know, is the flow of electrons through a conductor, such as a wire. Man has created a number of units to measure electricity. A measure of the actual flow of electrons is the electrical *current*. The current tells how many electrons move past a given point each second.

The unit of current is the *ampere*, named in honor of André M. Ampère (1775–1836), a pioneer in the study of electricity. One ampere is a flow of about 6.3 billion billion electrons per second. An average electric light bulb in your house uses about ½ ampere. A toaster uses about 5 amperes, and an electric iron requires twice that amount, about 10 amperes.

Before there can be a flow of current, though, there must be a *pressure*, a push, that sends the electrons flowing. The pressure in an electrical circuit comes from piling up more electrons at the negative pole of a battery or generator than at the positive pole. The difference in pressure results in the flow of electricity. It also explains why pressure is sometimes called *potential difference*.

The pressure, or potential difference, of an electrical circuit is measured in *volts*, named after Alessandro Volta (1745–1827). The wires coming into your house conduct electricity under an electrical pressure of about 115 or 120 volts.   The battery in an automobile produces either 6 or 12 volts, while a dry cell flashlight battery produces about 1½ volts.

Amperes and volts are closely related.   If you have two identical electrical circuits, the one with the greater voltage will have more amperes of current flowing.   But current and pressure are not the same.

Try this simple experiment, comparing electricity and water, to point up the difference between current flow and pressure.   You will need an empty coffee tin with a plastic cover.   Use a heavy nail to punch two holes in the side of the can, one above the other.   Make one near the bottom and one about halfway up.   Fill the can with water, and place the cover on securely.   Lay the can on its side so that the water comes out of the two holes.   You will note that the flow of water is just about the same through both holes.

Now fill the can with water again, and this time stand it upright.   Is the water flow from both holes the same this time?   No; more water is flowing out of the lower hole. The greater weight of the water above the lower hole creates a greater pressure at the lower level.   And the

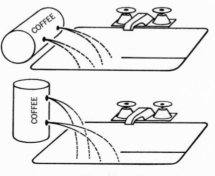

Coffee Can Experiment

greater pressure causes a greater rate of flow through the same size hole.

In electrical terms this tells you that in two identical circuits (two holes on side), if the voltage (pressure) is the same, the amperes (flow) will be the same. And if the voltage in one circuit is increased (can upright, lower hole), the amperes flowing will also increase.

What would happen if you were to make one large hole and one small hole in the coffee tin, fill it with water, and lay it on its side? Obviously, more water would flow through the larger hole, even though the pressure is the same. The smaller hole opposes or resists the flow of water, and therefore less passes through.

In electrical circuits, too, there is an opposition to the flow of electricity. It is called *resistance*. The unit of resistance is the *ohm*, named after Georg Ohm (1787–1854). A resistance of one ohm will allow one ampere of electricity to flow when a pressure of one volt is applied.

Resistance is the opposition to the flow of electricity. It is determined by the length, size, temperature, and nature of the conductor through which the electricity flows. (You recall that the change in resistance which occurs with a change in temperature is the basis for operation of the resistance thermometer.)

The resistance of one foot of copper wire with a diameter of $\frac{1}{1,000}$ of an inch, is 10.4 ohms. The same length and size of tungsten wire, the metal used in electric light bulbs, has a resistance of 33 ohms. And the same size wire of the alloy nichrome (nickel, chromium, iron, and manganese) which is used in electric toasters and heaters, has a resistance of 660 ohms.

There are, therefore, three measurements of electricity.

There is the flow of electricity or current, which is measured in amperes.   There is the pressure, or potential difference, which is measured in volts.   And there is the resistance, which is measured in ohms.

In 1826 Georg Ohm stated his famous law of electrical measurement which linked these three measurements:

$$\text{Current} = \frac{\text{Voltage}}{\text{Resistance}}$$

With Ohm's law, if you know two measurements of a circuit, you can always find the third.   If a circuit has a potential difference of 8 volts and a resistance of 2 ohms, how much current will flow?   Divide the 8 volts by the 2 ohms to get the answer, a current of 4 amperes.

Measuring Current

Most electrical measuring instruments make use of the fact that electricity flowing through a coil of wire creates a magnetic field around the coil.   When a compass, for example, is surrounded by a coil of wire carrying electricity, the needle moves away from north, indicating a magnetic field.

It is a simple matter to make an electromagnet so that you can see how it works.   You need a compass, a length of bell wire (thin, insulated copper wire), and a No. 6 dry cell.   Wrap several winds of the wire around the compass. Notice that this does not affect the compass needle. Now connect the two ends of the wire to the positive and negative poles of the dry cell.   As you do this, electricity flows through the wire, and the needle moves and points away from north.   Reverse the connections at the cell,

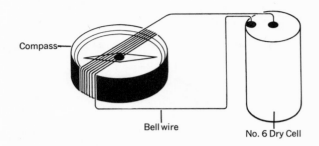

Compass

Bell wire

No. 6 Dry Cell

and you will find that the needle swings in the opposite direction.

This change of electrical energy (current in the wire), to mechanical energy (movement of the compass needle), is used in many electrical measuring instruments. The first such instrument for measuring electrical flow was the *galvanometer*, named for Luigi Galvani (1737–1798), one of the first electrical experimenters. It is a fundamental tool on which many others are based.

Your coil-wrapped compass is really a very simple galvanometer. The flow of electricity through the wire causes the magnetized compass needle to move. Very roughly speaking, the amount of movement of the needle is proportional to the amount of electricity flowing through the coil.

The laboratory galvanometer works on the same principle as your homemade model, but it is arranged in the opposite way. Your galvanometer has a movable magnet (the compass needle) inside a fixed coil. The laboratory galvanometer has a movable coil between the poles of a permanent magnet.

The galvanometer coil is a soft-iron frame wound with wire that is connected to the circuit being measured. A metal spring keeps the coil in a set position. When electricity flows through the coil of wire, the coil becomes an electromagnet, with its own north and south poles. The coil then tends to turn so that its magnetic field is parallel to that of the permanent magnet. A pointer is attached to the coil, so that it can show on a scale approximately how much electricity is flowing.

A galvanometer which is adjusted to measure the flow of electricity in amperes is called an *ammeter,* short for ampere meter. There are many designs of ammeters. The most popular type used for highly sensitive current measurements is the D'Arsonval ammeter, devised by Arsène D'Arsonval (1851–1940). This meter is really an advanced galvanometer. It has a movable coil between the poles of a permanent magnet. The coil is usually of very thin wire wound on a lightweight rectangular aluminum or copper frame, and supported on jewel bear-

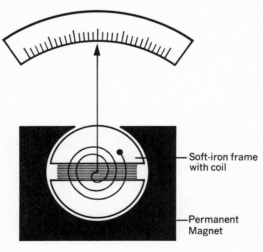

Soft-iron frame with coil

Permanent Magnet

Galvanometer

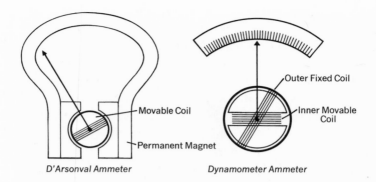

D'Arsonval Ammeter   Dynamometer Ammeter

ings to reduce friction.   As in the galvanometer, a pointer is attached to the coil.

When electricity flows through the coil, the coil becomes a temporary magnet.   The strength of the magnetic field is directly proportional to the electricity flowing through the coil.   It governs the movement of the pointer, and indicates the strength of the current in amperes.

The D'Arsonval ammeter may be used only to measure direct current (dc), current in one direction only.   It cannot measure alternating current (ac), in which the direction of current flow reverses itself many times each second.

The *dynamometer* or electrodynamometer is an ammeter that is more sensitive than the D'Arsonval ammeter and can measure both ac and dc.   In the dynamometer the permanent magnet is replaced by a coil within which the movable coil is placed.

The electricity being measured is sent through both the fixed and movable coils.   The fixed coil develops a magnetic field and the moving coil develops another magnetic field.   The two fields interact and the field of the moving coil tends to move parallel to the field of the fixed coil turning the movable coil. The greater the current, the greater the movement of the movable coil and its attached pointer.

The D'Arsonval ammeter is unable to measure alternating current because each time the direction of flow of electricity changes, the poles of the movable coil reverse and the pointer swings back and forth with the reversals of current.   In the dynamometer, both the movable and fixed coils reverse at the same time.   Since north to north is the same as south to south in two magnets, the dynamometer is able to measure the amperage of alternating current as well as of direct current.

Measuring Volts and Ohms

The instrument used to measure voltage is the *voltmeter*.   Basically, it is just like an ammeter.   The movement of the pointer, as in the ammeter, is proportional to the flow of electricity.   But the voltmeter is calibrated in volts, showing the potential difference which produces the current.

The major difference between the ammeter and voltmeter is resistance.   The ammeter has a very low resistance; the voltmeter has a very high resistance.   The high resistance makes it possible to measure voltage across any circuit with little electricity flowing through the voltmeter. It also protects the voltmeter from too great a flow of electricity.

The *potentiometer* is a tool that measures voltage by comparing the unknown voltage of the circuit with the known voltage given off by a standard voltage cell.   A resistor is used.   A resistor is a conductor whose resistance is known, and in some cases, can be changed.   The resistor is adjusted until the unknown voltage and the standard voltage cell are matched.   By noting the amount of resistance necessary to obtain balance, and considering the voltage from the standard cell, the unknown voltage is calculated.

For measuring resistance, the unknown resistor is balanced against a known resistor. It is similar to determining mass by balancing an unknown against a known mass.

The most popular and precise tool of resistance measurement is the *Wheatstone bridge*, named in honor of Sir Charles Wheatstone (1802–1875). In the Wheatstone bridge electricity is passed through four resistors, one of them being the unknown resistor being measured.

The current is divided into two paths. One path contains two of the resistors—one known, fixed resistor, and one known resistor whose resistance may be changed. The other path has another known resistor, and the unknown resistor. A bridge connects the junction of one path across to the junction of the other path, with a galvanometer placed on the bridge.

The changeable resistor is adjusted until the galvanometer reads zero, which indicates the same resistance in both paths. The bridge is then said to be in balance. Since the values of three of the four resistors are known, it is a simple matter to find the value of the unknown resistor once the bridge is in balance.

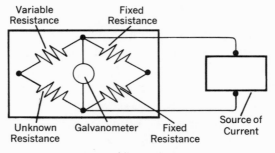

Wheatstone Bridge

Electrical Standards

The definition of the standard ampere was arrived at by the process of electrolysis. In electrolysis, electrodes connected to the positive and negative poles of a current source, such as a battery or house line, are placed in a metal salt solution. As the electricity flows through the salt solution, the metal that is in solution is deposited on the negative electrode.

The standard ampere, then, is the amount of steady current that will deposit silver on the negative electrode at the rate of 0.001118 grams ($\frac{1}{25,000}$ of an ounce) per second, from a solution of silver nitrate in water. In 1948 the ampere was redefined so that this amount of current is now considered to be 0.99985 absolute amperes. A small change indeed, but one that must be considered in modern measurements.

To set the national standard of the ampere, an instrument called a *current balance* is used. It is built around a balance that is no different from the one used in mass measurements. From one of the pans a coil of wire is suspended which can move up and down within, but not touching, a larger fixed coil. Both coils are connected to a source of electrical current. Above the other pan is a device that can raise or lower a weight onto the pan.

The electrical circuit is so arranged that the balance is in equilibrium when the current flows in one direction through both coils. When the current in the fixed coil is reversed, it pulls down on the movable coil, and on the pan to which it is attached. At the same time a weight is lowered onto the other pan, to balance the pull of the coil. By

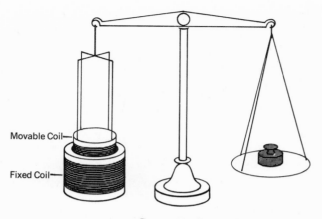

Current Balance

noting exactly how much weight is necessary to achieve a balance, and by knowing the size of the coils, the exact amount of current can be determined.

The voltage cells, the standard source of voltage, were the carefully guarded treasure in the station wagon trip to the new buildings of the National Bureau of Standards. At the National Bureau these cells are kept in a special oil bath, at a temperature of 28° C, a temperature which is not allowed to vary by more than a few thousandths of a degree.   It is interesting that Dr. Walter Hamer, who is in charge of the cells which require such great care and patience, raises orchids at home, a hobby which also requires the greatest care and patience.

The delicate voltage standard is a glass vial in the shape of the letter H.   At the bottom of one leg is the cathode of mercury and mercurous sulfate.   At the bottom of the other leg is the anode, an amalgam of mercury and cadmium.   Throughout the vial is a saturated solution of cadmium sulfate, including crystals of cadmium sulfate.

The saturated cadmium cells produce a voltage of approximately one volt, or to be more precise, 1.018366 volts at 20° C. Just as with the ampere, a new absolute volt was redefined in 1948 so that one old volt equaled 1.00034 absolute volts. In 1969 another slight change was made, so that one 1948 volt now equals 1.000010 new volts. Since no current is drawn off, the voltage in the cells stays remarkably stable. Eleven of the cells at the National Bureau of Standards date back to 1906, and have not changed since then.

The cells are constantly being examined to ensure that they are not changing. Occasionally the voltage of a cell

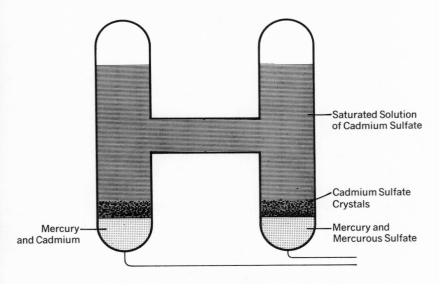

Voltage Cell

will start to drift, or the cell may even stop producing voltage altogether.   Because of this element of risk, no one cell is the national standard.   Rather there is a group of about 40 cells, called the National Reference Group.   If one of this group misbehaves, it is replaced by a cell from a group of cells kept as secondary standards.   Someday, it is hoped, there will be an atomic source of the standard volt that will make it unnecessary to maintain the delicate, sensitive saturated cadmium cells.

The standard of electrical resistance, the ohm, was defined at the International Electrical Congress in 1893. The ohm is the resistance to current of a column of mercury 106.3 centimeters long and one square millimeter in cross section, at a temperature of $0°$ C.   In other words, if the column of mercury is thought of as a wire, the resistance of the mercury "wire" to the flow of electricity through it is one ohm.   The ohm, too, was changed in 1948 so that the old ohm is equal to 1.00049 new absolute ohms.

The working standards of resistance at the National Bureau of Standards are resistor coils made of the alloy manganin, containing copper (84 per cent), manganese (12 per cent), and nickel (4 per cent).   The manganin is remarkably stable in its resistance.   It also shows a direct change in resistance with any change in length or thickness. Therefore, by carefully measuring the dimensions of the manganin coil, it is possible to calculate its resistance, and to know that other coils with the same dimensions will have the same resistance.

Over the years there has been a search for an instrument that would give more precise measurements of resistance than the manganin resistors.   Since 1961 the National Bureau of Standards has used a special capacitor or condenser for its standard resistance measurements.

A capacitor is a device in which two parallel metal plates are separated by an insulating material of some sort. An electrical charge can be built up on one of the plates of the capacitor, and the amount of this charge can be very accurately calculated by measuring the size of the capacitor plates. By building a circuit which includes a standard capacitor and the resistor being tested, extremely accurate measurements of the unknown resistance can be made.

Electric Power and Energy

To most of us, electricity is more than the movement of electrons through a circuit. It is our most useful servant. It runs everything from the electric toothbrush we use in the morning to giant locomotives. This is electric power.

Power is the rate or speed of doing work. The unit of power is the *watt*, named in honor of James Watt (1736–1819), inventor of the steam engine. The power of an electrical circuit (watts) is equal to the current (amperes), times the pressure (volts). It should, therefore, be possible to measure power by using an ammeter and a voltmeter, and multiplying the results. The *wattmeter* does this in one operation.

The wattmeter is similar in construction to the dynamometer. There is a fixed coil that is connected so that its strength is proportional to the current, or amperes. A movable coil is connected so that its strength is proportional to the pressure, or volts. The movement of the movable coil is the product of the amperes and volts—which is the watts. A pointer attached to the movable coil indicates the watts, or power of the circuit.

The companies that generate electricity and then sell it base the charges to their customers on how many watts of power are used, and for how many hours. This is electrical energy. Energy equals power multiplied by time. This unit of energy is the *watt-hour*, which is the power of one watt for one hour.

Electric companies measure the energy used by their customers with a *watt-hour meter*, popularly called an electric meter. You can probably find one in a round glass case near where the electric lines enter your house.

The watt-hour meter differs from the wattmeter in the arrangement of the movable coil. In the wattmeter, the coil turns to a point, and remains there. In the watt-hour meter, the coil actually rotates, and continues to rotate as long as energy is being used. The speed of rotation is proportional to the amount of energy.

Attached to the moving coil are gears which move pointers on small dials. To find the total amount of power used since the last reading, the meter reader jots down the last number passed by the pointer of each dial. Since the watt-hour is a very small unit for measuring electricity consumed in a home, the meter shows the amount used in kilowatt-hours, 1,000 watt-hours. From right to left each figure on the dials shows kilowatt-hours in 10s, 100s, 1,000s, and 10,000s. The charge on your electric bill is computed by subtracting the last meter reading from the one before, and multiplying the result by the rate per kilowatt-hour charged by the electric company.

Although there is a very wide range of electrical measuring devices from the highly complex electrical measurement tools of the standards laboratory to the kilowatt-hour meter in your home, all use one of two basic principles.   In one type, the electric energy is changed into mechanical energy by means of electromagnets.   The amount of mechanical movement is then measured.   The galvanometer, ammeter, voltmeter, wattmeter, and watthour meter are of this kind.

The other type, such as the potentiometer, Wheatstone bridge, and current balance, use a balance method in which a known electrical quantity is made to equal the unknown quantity.   The amount of adjustment necessary to achieve balance is a measure of electrical energy.

ten ▪ *Radiation Measurement*

IN THE 1950s science entered the Atomic Age. The Atomic Age is based on a more complete understanding of the atom, with its heavy nucleus containing protons and neutrons, and its light electrons circling the nucleus. The number of positive protons is equal to the number of negative electrons, making the atom electrically neutral.

With this understanding came the first splitting of the atom, nuclear reactors, and the atom bomb. Since then, many other ways of putting the atom to work for man have been found. Nuclear reactors now power ships and submarines, and furnish whole cities with electricity. Atomic chemicals are used to diagnose and treat many diseases. Atomic science enables biologists to study the basis of life within the cell, chemists to understand the nature of chemical reactions, and physicists to search for the fundamental particles of matter. Atomic science is one of the most important and fastest growing fields of science.

Of particular interest to the atomic scientists are certain atoms which are not stable, which do not stay the same. The nuclei (plural of nucleus) of these atoms break down, or decay. As they decay, they send out tiny bits of matter, called particles, and tiny bursts of energy, called rays. This process of nuclear decay is called *radioactivity*.

Radioactivity is one of the most challenging and important measurements of atomic science.   No one can see, feel, hear—or even smell—radioactivity, even though it can be extremely dangerous to man.   The growth of atomic science is largely based on recognizing and measuring radioactivity.   In a very short time atomic scientists have developed many excellent measuring tools and methods.

Curies, Roentgens, and Rads

The rate at which particles and rays are emitted from a source gives the unit of radioactive measurement.   The unit is the *curie*, named after Marie Curie (1867–1934), one of the early workers in radioactivity, and the discoverer of radium.   The curie is defined as the quantity of a radioactive source that emits 37 billion particles and rays per second.   One gram (about ⅒ of an ounce) of radium produces approximately one curie of radioactivity.

Some of the particles and rays are emitted as the result of natural radioactivity.   Radium and uranium, for example, are naturally radioactive.   They continually pour out a stream of particles and rays from within their atoms.

Some other elements can be made artificially radioactive by changing their atomic structure in some way.   Artificially radioactive elements also emit various atomic particles and rays.   In addition, man-made atomic devices, such as atom smashers or nuclear reactors, also produce their own types of atomic radiation.

Although there are many different kinds of atomic radiation, three particles, the *alpha particle*, the *beta particle*, and the *neutron*, and two types of rays, the *gamma ray* and the *X ray*, are the usual subjects for measurements.

The alpha particle is the largest and heaviest of these

particles. It consists of two protons and two neutrons, the particles found within the nucleus of the atom. The beta particle is nothing more than an electron. It is very much lighter than the alpha particle. The neutron is one of the particles found in the nucleus of most atoms.

The gamma rays are waves of electromagnetic energy that are emitted from the nucleus of an atom. X rays are similar waves that come from activity in the electrons that surround the nucleus. These rays are the same as radio waves or light waves, except that the wavelengths of the gamma rays and X rays are very much shorter. Compared to visible light waves, which range from $1/60,000$ of an inch to $1/30,000$ of an inch, X rays are about 10,000 times shorter, and gamma rays are one-million times shorter.

Have you ever had an X-ray picture taken of your teeth or of a broken bone? The X ray is a valuable medical tool —but it is also very dangerous. Accurate measurement of exposure to X rays is necessary to protect the health of those who study and use X rays, as well as those who are occasionally exposed to X rays for medical reasons.

The unit of exposure to radiation is the *roentgen,* named after Wilhelm Roentgen (1845–1923), the discoverer of X rays. The roentgen is defined by the electrostatic charge the X rays or gamma rays create. One roentgen is an exposure to X or gamma rays that creates one unit of electrostatic charge in 0.001,293 grams of air. (An electrostatic charge is defined so that two positive charges, one centimeter apart in a vacuum, repel each other with a force of one dyne.) The roentgen is a very small unit. It takes, for instance, exposure to 100,000 roentgens to warm one gram of air by 1° C.

X rays and gamma rays interact with the atoms of any

material through which they pass. Atoms are always electrically balanced, the positive protons balancing the negative electrons. When X rays or gamma rays pass through the air, for example, they collide with some of the circling electrons of the atoms of the air molecules. The electrons are knocked free.

When an atom loses an electron, it remains with a positive charge, while the free electron has a negative charge. The positive atom and the negative electron are called *ions.* The ions give a charge to the air. By measuring this charge the amount of exposure to radiation, in roentgens, can be found.

But when studying the effects of X and gamma rays on human beings, it is not enough to know the exposure. It is also necessary to know how much energy is absorbed by the body from the radiation striking it. The energy absorbed is called the radiation dose. The unit of radiation dose is the *rad,* an acronym of radiation absorbed dose. One rad is defined as 100 ergs of absorbed energy per gram. This is approximately the energy absorbed per gram of soft tissue exposed to one roentgen of X radiation. The rads are found by measuring the exposure in roentgens and computing that with the weight of the body.

Man in his lifetime receives between seven and ten rads from the natural environment; that is, from cosmic rays, and from radioactive sources in food and air, and in rocks and soil. It is believed that this dose is responsible for a certain number of cases of cancer and birth defects every year. The maximum additional dose allowed for workers in atomic laboratories is between 12 and 15 rads, received over an entire year. A single dose of 500 rads will kill a man.

Electrical Ion Detectors

All radiation measuring instruments are arranged so that the atomic radiation being studied either passes through or strikes some material—liquid, solid, or gas. The different particles and rays create ions in the target material.

In some devices the ions start an electrical current, which can be measured with an electrical meter. In other devices the ions cause flashes of light, which can be counted with a phototube. Still other devices photograph a trail of tiny water drops or bubbles left by the ions. Since in all of these instruments the ion production is proportional to the radiation, a measure of the ions produced is easily changed into a measure of the amount and type of radiation being received.

Have you ever seen a picture of a scientist carrying a small metal box as he enters an area that is "hot" with radiation? He is probably carrying a Geiger counter, or more correctly, a *Geiger-Müller tube*. In the Geiger-Müller tube, the ions created by the radiation produce short pulses of electricity. This instrument is named after Hans Geiger (1882–1945), who first devised the tool in 1908, and E. W. Müller, who helped Geiger improve it in 1928.

The Geiger-Müller tube consists of a cylindrical metal tube, with a thin wire running down the center. The walls of the tube are connected to the negative pole of a source of high voltage. The center wire is connected to the positive pole. A large voltage, from 600 volts, exists between the walls and the center wire. The distance from the wall to the wire is great enough to prevent the current

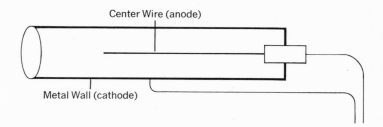

Center Wire (anode)

Metal Wall (cathode)

from jumping across. The tube is filled with either argon or neon gas.

When an alpha or beta particle, or a gamma or X ray, passes through the tube, it knocks electrons off some of the gas atoms, creating ions. The ions cause a pulse of current to jump from the wall to the wire. This pulse can then be used to make a click in a loudspeaker, or to flash a light, or to be counted in an electronic circuit. The pulses are all of the same size.

Another radiation detector, similar to the Geiger-Müller tube, is the *ionization chamber*. Usually the ionization chamber is filled with air, rather than a gas as in the Geiger-Müller tube. As with the Geiger-Müller tube, the walls of the ionization chamber are given a negative electrical charge.

The central collector, usually a rod instead of a wire, has a positive electrical charge. The potential difference between the wall and the center rod of the ionization chamber, though, is much lower than in the Geiger-Müller tube. It is only about two hundred volts. Because of the lower voltage, the ionization chamber is usually used to measure the average current produced by the ions, rather than the pulses as in the Geiger-Müller tube.

The two biggest uses of the ionization chamber are to measure X rays, and to count the flow of neutrons in a nuclear reactor. Neutrons do not create ions as easily as the other particles. This difficulty is overcome by filling the chamber with a compound of boron. The neutrons create ions as they collide with the molecules of the boron compound.

You might compare the ionization chamber to a ball (ion) rolling down a gentle hill (low voltage) to a valley (collecting rod). It follows then that the next detector, the *proportional counter,* is like a snowball rolling down a snow covered mountain. In the ionization chamber the ions fall by themselves; in the proportional counter the ions start avalanches, creating more ions as they rush to the collecting rod.

The proportional counter has a much higher voltage than the ionization chamber. It pulls the ions so strongly to the center rod that they have enough energy to create still other ions. It is possible to create up to 100,000 ions for every particle or ray that enters the proportional counter. By counting the number of ions, it is possible to calculate the number of particles or rays striking the proportional counter, as well as to measure their energy.

Visual Ion Detectors

The oldest method of radiation measurement, in fact the way radioactivity was discovered, is *photography.* Just before the turn of the century, Antoine Henri Becquerel (1852–1908), found that crystals of uranium were able to fog sheets of photographic paper that were shielded from all visible light.

You can try this out, using a handy, safe source of radiation that is found in most homes. The glowing numbers on clocks or watches usually contain a small amount of a radioactive material. Take a small sheet of photographic contact printing paper, and keeping it in its lightproof wrapping, place it face down on a clock or watch with glowing numbers.

Put the clock and the paper away in a dark place. Leave it there for several hours or overnight. When you have the picture printed, you will find white areas on the picture—even though the paper was not ex-

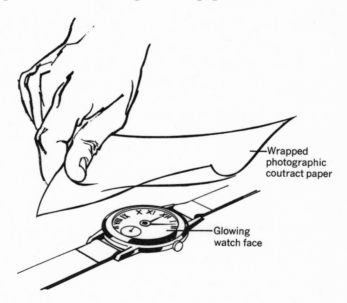

Wrapped photographic coutract paper

Glowing watch face

posed to visible light. The radiation from the glowing numbers was able to pass through the paper wrapping and fog the photographic paper.

One important use of photography is in the badges pinned to the lab coats of scientists and workers who are exposed to atomic radiation. The badge consists of a plastic holder containing a section of photographic film. The film incorporates various materials, and is partly covered with special shielding, so that any particle or ray that strikes the badge will show up on the film when it is developed. In this way the exposure to radiation can be measured for the personnel in atomic laboratories, and steps can be taken to prevent overexposure.

Your wrist watch with glowing numbers is also a simple radiation detector, called a *scintillation counter.* Take the watch into a dark room, and after your eyes adjust to the dark, look at the numbers through a magnifying glass. What do you see? Rather than a steady glow, you see many tiny flashes of light. These flashes of light are called scintillations.

The numbers on the watch are covered with a mixture of two chemicals—one that emits radiation (such as a compound containing a small amount of radium), and one (such as zinc sulfide), that gives off a flash of light whenever it is struck by an atomic particle. The radium compound is continually emitting particles. These particles ionize the atoms of the zinc sulfide, causing scintillations. The rapid scintillations make the numbers appear to be glowing.

In the laboratory scintillation counter, different substances, solid or liquid, can be used for the target material that will emit scintillations. It is also more practical to have the source of radiation separate, and not mixed in with the scintillating materials. And most scintillation counters have an automatic device to count the number of scintillations.

The most widely used material in the scintillation counter is the crystal sodium iodide, to which a trace of thallium has been added. Usually the crystal is mounted directly on the face of a phototube, so that all of the scintillations are picked up by the phototube. Quite often a special type of phototube is used in which the pulse of current created by the scintillation is multiplied within the tube. A much stronger burst of current emerges. This type of phototube is called a *photomultiplier*.

Scintillation counters are very important in the fields of medicine and medical research. For example, a valuable

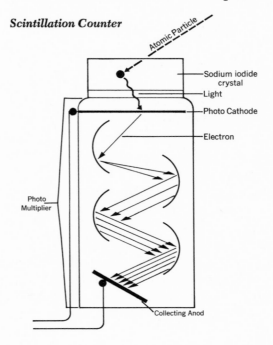

Scintillation Counter

Atomic Particle

Sodium iodide crystal

Light

Photo Cathode

Electron

Photo Multiplier

Collecting Anod

new method of diagnosing several diseases is to feed the patient some radioactive material. The material is tracked as it passes through the patient's body. By noting where it goes and how long it takes to get there, the doctor is able to make a diagnosis of disease in some cases, and to pinpoint the exact trouble spot in others.

Most of the detectors used for medical purposes are scintillation counters made with sodium iodide crystals. Sometimes, however, the doctor wants a count of the emission from the entire body. In these cases a liquid scintillation counter is used. The liquid, a widely used one is called POPOP, is in a tank built to surround a person. Just as with sodium iodide, POPOP emits a flash of light every time it is struck by a particle or ray. A phototube is used to detect the scintillations.

One of the first whole-body liquid scintillation counters was put on display at an atomic science fair in Geneva, Switzerland, in 1955. Visitors were invited to enter the counter and have their radiation measured. One interesting side result was to note which people ignored instructions and had not removed their radium dial watches. Another bonus was in detecting a sample of uranium in the pocket of a boy who had taken it from another exhibit.

In 1911, C. T. R. Wilson (1869–1959), a British scientist, invented the *cloud chamber*, one of the most valuable tools of radiation measurement. He was the first to use the understanding of cloud and rain formation for the purpose of measuring radiation.

It was known that air at any temperature can contain only a certain amount of moisture or water vapor. If the temperature of the air drops, it cannot contain as much water vapor. The water vapor then condenses around

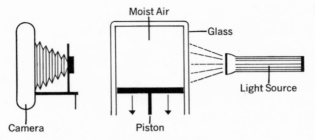

Wilson's Cloud Chamber

specks of dust, becoming fine drops of water, or clouds. If the drops become large enough they fall down as rain.

The cloud chamber is filled with air containing as much water vapor as possible. The bottom of the chamber is a movable piston. When the piston is suddenly lowered, the volume of the chamber increases, which causes the temperature of the air inside to drop. The water vapor is ready to condense. There are no dust particles in the cloud chamber. Therefore, if an atomic particle should pass through at that moment, tiny droplets of water will form along the trail of the particle.

In Wilson's cloud chamber, a light is shone through glass windows in the top or wall of the chamber. A camera photographs the trail of water droplets, making a permanent record of the path of the particle. The length of the path, the size of the droplets, and how the path behaves if magnets are placed around the cloud chamber—all these tell the type, energy, mass, and electrical charge of the particle.

A recent improvement on the cloud chamber is the *diffusion chamber*. In the diffusion chamber, alcohol vapor is released in the upper part of the chamber. The entire chamber is set on dry ice, keeping the bottom part at a very low temperature, about −77° C. The alcohol vapor spreads, or diffuses, filling the entire chamber. When it reaches the lower, colder part, it is ready to condense on any available particle. In this way there is no need for the piston of the cloud chamber. The diffusion chamber shows the trails of atomic particles whenever they pass through, not only when the chamber is suddenly cooled.

You can make your own simple diffusion chamber. You will need a glass jar with a wide neck, a metal cover, and a rubber gasket in the cover. You will also need scraps of black velvet and felt of any color, alcohol, a cake of dry ice, and a light source.

Cut out a circle of black velvet that will fit within the cap but not touch the gasket. Glue it into position. Cut a circle out of the felt, with a hole in the center. Glue this to the bottom of the jar. Allow the glue in both places to dry thoroughly before proceeding with the experiment.

When you are sure that the glue is dry, drip tablespoons of alcohol on the felt until it is completely soaked. Place the cover on the jar, screwing it on as tightly as possible.

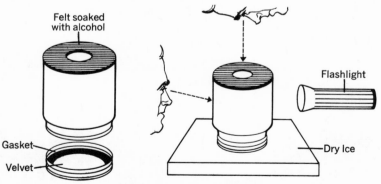

Diffusion Chamber Experiment

(The experiment will not work if any air can get in.) Turn the jar over and place it so that the metal cap is resting on the dry ice.

Shine a good, well-focused light, a flashlight or microscope light with a diameter beam of about one inch will do, just above the velvet. Make your observations through the hole in the felt or from the side of the jar opposite the light source.

Do you see short tracks of droplets forming in the fog inside the jar? If you do each step very carefully, you should be able to see tracks caused by natural radiation passing through the diffusion chamber.

Closely related to the cloud chamber is the *bubble chamber*, built in 1952 by the American scientist Donald A. Glaser (born 1926). If an atomic particle passes through the special liquid in the bubble chamber at the same instant that the volume of the chamber is suddenly increased by a movable piston, the particle will leave a trail of bubbles through the liquid. The path can then be photographed and studied in the same way as the droplets in the cloud chamber.

The world's largest bubble chamber is at the target end of one of the giant atom smashers at the Brookhaven National Laboratory. It has a chamber 80 inches long, filled with 240 gallons of liquid hydrogen, kept at a temperature of $-412°$ F. It took four years to build and cost nearly 6 million dollars to complete in 1963.

Bubble Chamber

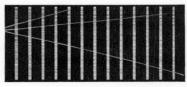

Spark Chamber

With the 80-inch bubble chamber, atomic scientists have been taking about 3 million photographs a year of the results of atom smashing experiments. A phototube "reads" these pictures, and feeds the information to a computer, which interprets the tracks. The bubble chamber made possible the discovery, in 1964, of a subatomic particle (the omega-minus hyperon), which had been predicted in theory, but which had never actually been seen. One of the difficulties of finding this particle was that it has a total lifetime of one ten-billionth of a second!

The *spark chamber* is also used in advanced research on atomic particles. It consists of a series of electrically charged parallel aluminum plates, placed in a gas-filled chamber. When a charged particle enters the spark chamber, a spark jumps between the plates along the path of the particle. The spark chamber and the bubble chamber are the newer visual ion detectors. They have been replacing the older cloud and diffusion chambers.

Probability

Tossing coins and trying to guess the results may seem very different from measuring radiation in a scientific laboratory. But actually they are very closely related. The emission of particles or rays by atoms is a matter of chance or probability. Whether a coin lands heads or tails is likewise a matter of chance and probability.

The laws of probability make it possible to predict the most likely outcome of future events. And the more events that are observed, the closer the results will approach the prediction of the probability.

If, for instance, you could observe a single atom of uranium, you would have no way of knowing when it would emit an alpha particle. The laws of probability, though, tell us that if you have 5 billion billion atoms of uranium 238, one of them will emit a particle within one second.

But this is a probability, not a certainty. There is no way to know which atom will emit the particle during any specific second. It might be that two alpha particles will be emitted the first second, and none during the next second; or none during the first hour and twice as many during the next hour; or any combination that averages out, if enough observations are made, to one emission per second. The longer the period of observation, the closer will the rate approach one per second.

The situation is the same with tossing a coin. Half the tosses should be heads and half tails. If you toss just a few times your results are very uncertain. After thousands of trys you get closer to half heads, half tails. A million tosses will bring you closer yet. The more times you try, the closer you get to half and half.

Radiation measurements are possible because they deal with samples of radioactive material that contain millions and millions of individual atoms. When dealing with this quantity of atoms, the laws of probability can be used to arrive at very accurate results.

You can test the laws of probability with this experiment in coin tossing. The results of tossing four coins at once should be in the ratio of one toss of four heads or four tails, to four tosses of three heads and one tail or three tails and one head, to six tosses of two heads and two tails.

On a piece of paper make a column for each of the five possible results—4 heads, 3 heads/1 tail, 2 heads/2 tails, 1 head/3 tails, 4 tails. Toss all four coins at once, marking the result in the correct column. Do it for ten tosses. How do your results compare with the probability? Are they close?

Try it over and over again. Total your results as you go along. Do your results get closer to the predicted probability? As in all observations of probability, the more examples that are used, the more likely it is that you will approach the expected probability.

The laws of probability make it possible to predict the rate of radioactive emission. They also make it possible to predict how many observations will differ from the expected rate, and by how much. This is possible because chance events, such as radioactive emission or coin tossing, follow definite patterns, called the normal distribution of error. The laws of probability and error, the large samples involved, and the many observations that have been made, have allowed the chance nature of radioactive radiation to be made into a precise science.

Epilogue

ABOUT EIGHTY YEARS AGO, most physicists believed that they had a true understanding of the physical world. All that remained for the future, it seemed, was to add more details to what was already known, and to make even finer measurements. There was no reason to doubt that measurement would continue to improve.

Physicists knew that in all measurements there is an interaction between the object being measured and the measuring device. When you measure an electric current, some of the current flows through the meter, changing the original value of the current. When you measure the temperature of a liquid, the thermometer changes the temperature of the liquid. As the precision of measurement increased, so did the significance of these changes. The task was to find ways to measure the changes.

As the physicists were following this line of research, a German physicist came along in 1927, and completely destroyed the basis of much of their work. In that year, young Werner Heisenberg (born 1901), stated his uncertainty principle. He put forward his belief, along with strong supporting evidence, that there was a definite limit to man's measuring ability. And as a result, there was a definite limit to man's knowledge of the physical world!

He extended ordinary measurements to the atomic level. In an imaginary "thought experiment" he showed that both the position and velocity of an atomic particle cannot be measured with very high precision. Furthermore he worked out a formula that showed how the increase in the accuracy of one measurement leads to a decrease in the accuracy of the other.

What does the uncertainty principle mean to the science of measurement? Will metrology be able to continue the steady advance that has taken place over 10,000 years or are we approaching the limit of measurement? Is there a level, as defined by the uncertainty principle, beyond which we cannot progress?

Index